SONGIFTS

M·U·S·I·C

An Offering in Song & Worship

JEANNE HARPER
Christopher Norton · Roland Fudge
Jane Harris

HODDER AND STOUGHTON
LONDON SYDNEY AUCKLAND TORONTO

Copyright Information

Every effort has been made to trace the owners of copyright material included in this collection, and full acknowledgement is printed alongside each song. The publishers would welcome details of any errors or omissions, which will be incorporated into future reprints.

ISBN 0 340 38169 8

Hodder and Stoughton Editorial Office: 47 Bedford Square, London WC1B 3DP.

Contents

Preface

Since the sixties God has been leading many in the Churches to a fresh understanding and experience of the Holy Spirit, both individually and corporately. Now we can see God's longing for intimacy of worship, and then catch the vision of Him enthroned in His majesty. My prayer is that this worship, as on the day of Pentecost, will overflow to the whole world.

We are all dependent on each other, and this is true of both Churches and nations. This book invites us to be open to other cultures, so that we may all share the different gifts the Spirit is giving worldwide. So let us discover, for instance, the joyful swinging rhythm of African call-and-answer songs (no. 63), sense the stark harmony and joyful determination of persecuted Greek believers (no. 81), enter into the abandon of the Israelis in "Hallelujah" (no. 11), the freshness of faith in three songs from the Republic of China (nos. 51, 77, 94), the serenity and depth of contributions from Scandinavia and Iran (nos. 1, 30, 72). Let us be open to the brisk swing from the Caribbean (no. 91), and the Spanish lilt of 'heaven is singing" (no. 12).

This is a book for participation, rather than solo or group songs. It is for this reason the emphasis is on simplicity in piano arrangements and lyrics and melodies — though there is plenty for the enterprising to enlarge upon and enjoy.

The more familiar songs are put together in medleys: memorising the words of these is encouraged for the sake of flow in worship. In the text composers and authors are combined at the head, the author's name being consistently below that of the composer throughout. The appendices include various suggestions to enhance worship and to assist selections of songs, and one should study these in order to make full use of SONGIFTS. Please note that where verses of a song have more syllables than are in its first verse, it will be necessary to add the required extra notes. We have chosen this method to avoid cluttering the text with bracketed notes.

May we all share the varied experiences of God's people in many lands as we explore and enjoy this book.

Jeanne Harper
Stanfords, September 1985

Acknowledgements

I am extremely indebted to Christopher Norton of "Ears & Eyes" for the enormous amount of work he has done in arranging songs, to Roland Fudge for his invaluable advice, his own personal contribution in songs and arrangements, and the whole task he has undertaken in recording the songs, to Jane Harris for her faithful work in copying and her help in many ways throughout the time of the compiling of the book. I want to thank my husband for his unstinted support during these two years, and for his expert management of the business side of the book. I am most grateful to Edward England for his encouragement and wisdom at all times. My grateful thanks to Valeria Fairhead for her lovely illustrations and lastly to the book's sponsors who have helped with advice and have backed me from the start: Connie Sharp of St. John's Church, Harborne, Birmingham, Graham Cray and Andrew Maries of St. Michael-le-Belfrey Church, York, Pete Meadows of Spring Harvest, Clive Calver of the Evangelical Alliance, John Marsh of St. Thomas' Church, Sheffield, and Anne Townsend of the Care Trust.

SONGIFTS

1

Songs of Praise and Thanksgiving

1. All I am will sing out

(Jas vill ge dig o Herre, min lovsang)

Christer Hultgren
Transl. Jeanne Harper
Arr. Christopher Norton

♩ = 112

With joyful abandon

mf 1. All I am will sing out as a praise song, ev - ery
2. There is no - bo - dy else who is wor - thy, — to
mp 3. If at times through my si - lence I grieve You, if through

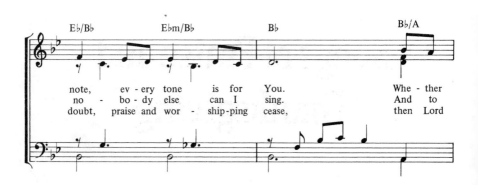

note, ev - ery tone is for You. Whe - ther
no - bo - dy else can I sing. And to
doubt, praise and wor - ship-ping cease, then Lord

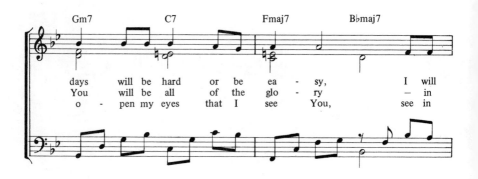

days will be hard or be ea - sy, I will
You will be all of the glo - ry — in
o - pen my eyes that I see You, see in

2. All you that are righteous

Sarah Lacy
Arr. Christopher Norton

3. Be blessed

T. Hamilton
Arr. Jeanne Harper

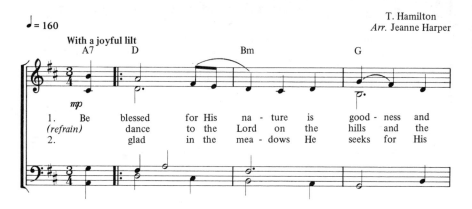

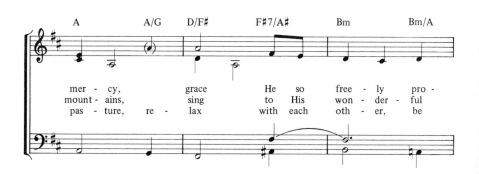

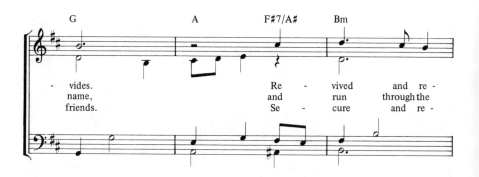

This fresh country song is popular in Norway and reflects the joy of welcoming spring after the long winter.

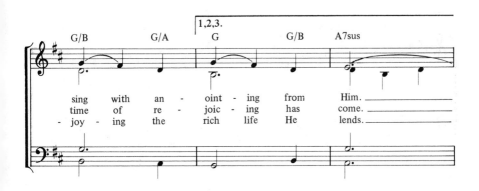

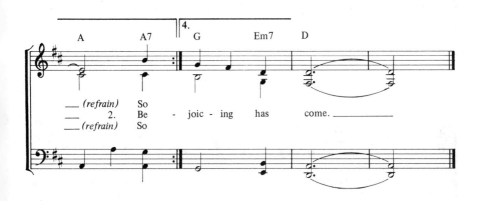

4. Bring a psalm

Capo 3 (Dm)

♩ = 108

Brent Chambers

With verve

Bring a psalm to the Lord, from the Spi-rit and from His Word, lift your voice and re-joice, for our God is a might-y King. So come and clap your hands, raise a shout, as we stand before the

5. Every breath that I take

♩ = 120

Eddie Espinosa
Arr. James Gabriel Stipech

1. Ev-'ry breath that I take __ says I __ love You __
2. Ev-'ry day that goes by __ shows Your __ mer-cy __

and ev-'ry beat of my heart says I'm Yours. __
and ev-'ry gift that You give shows You care. __

Ev-'ry step that I take __ says I __ need You __
Ev-'ry song that I sing __ says You're __ wor-thy __

and I will bless Your ho ly name. __

You are my re - dee - mer,

6. Finnish song of joy

Traditional
Aino Piirola
Arr. and Transl. Jeanne Harper

This song is part of a folk mass. Its joyful abandon has a Jewish flavour.

7. For you and me

8. God is good

Capo 3 (Em)

♩ = 138

Graham Kendrick

9. God of glory

Descant Derek Kidner
Henry Smart 1813-79 "Regent Square"
Christine Dare

♩ = 96

Majestically

Descant

5. Ri-sen, reign-ing, glor - ious Sa - viour, com-ing on the

1. God of glo - ry, power and splen-dour, God en - throned in
2. Ru - ler of the heav'n - ly pla - ces, to the earth You
3. In Your love - ly face, Lord Je - sus, shines the Fa - ther's

clouds with power, one day ev-'ry tongue will bless You,

ma - jest - y, light trans - cen - dent, truth res-plen-dent,
came to die, left Your Fa - ther's shin - ing pre-sence
ra - dianc - y, pour - ing out up - on Your peo-ple

ev - 'ry knee to You will bow. We a-dore You, bow be-

in - carn - a - tion myst - e - ry, we a - dore You
came in great hu - mi - li - ty, we a - dore You
grace and truth e - tern - al - ly, we a - dore You

- fore ____ You, crown You, Je - sus, ____

bow be - fore You, glo - rious Sa - viour,
bow be - fore You, glo - rious Sa - viour,
bow be - fore You, glo - rious Sa - viour,

Last time to Coda ⊕

⊕ *CODA*

Lord ____ and King.

Lord and King.
Lord and King.
Lord and King.

Verse 4: Come and reign in us Lord Jesus,
Cleanse our lives in every part,
Fill us with Your Holy Spirit,
Be the light in every heart.
We adore You, bow before You,
Praise You as our Lord and King.

Verse 5: Risen, reigning, glorious Saviour,
Coming on the clouds with power,
One day every tongue will bless You,
Every knee to You will bow.
We adore You, bow before You,
Crown You, Jesus, Lord and King.

10. Great and wonderful

Stuart Dauermann
Arr. Roland Fudge

11. Hallelujah

Capo 3 (G)

♩ = 100

Shimrit Orr *and* Kobi Oshrat
Arr. Christopher Norton

This song from Israel won the Eurovision song contest for 1982 and has travelled far beyond the bounds of Christian circles.

12. Heaven is singing

Capo 3 (Am)

♩ = 88 *(and increasing in speed)*

Pablo Sosa
Arr. Jeanne Harper

Lively and rhythmic

1. Hea - ven is sing - ing for joy ___ 'All - e - lu - ia,' for in your life and __ mine is shi - ning the glo - ry of God.
2. Hea - ven is sing - ing for joy ___ 'All - e - lu - ia,' for your__ life and __ mine are one __ in the glo - ry of God.
3. Hea - ven is sing - ing for joy ___ 'All - e - lu - ia,' for your__ life and __ mine will al - ways pro- claim _____ the Lord.

All - e - lu - ia, All - e - lu - ia,

All - e - lu - ia, All - e - lu - ia!

This song is sung with many repeats in quick succession and ending in the major.

13. How great is our God
(medley)

What a mighty God: Zulu working song.

Unknown
Arrs. Jeanne Harper, Peter Sandwall

and He said 'I'll ne - ver leave _____ you,

put your trust in Me.'

1. What a
2. He cre -

might - y God we serve, _____ what a
- a - ted you and me, _____ He cre -

might - y God we serve, _____ what a
- a - ted you and me, _____ He cre -

14. Hymn of glory

Capo 3 (A)
♩.=69

Boldly, with pulsating rhythm

Charles Christmas
Arr. Charles High

1. Give thanks to our God ___ and let Him be praised with sanc-ti-fied hearts ___ and hands that are raised. ___ Come, join a song of praise to our God.
2. His word ev - er true, ___ the Son of His love. ___ Sing, men of earth, to the heav-ens a - bove. Hon-our and glo-ry be-long to our God.
3. Wor-thy the Lamb Who was slain for our sins. ___ He laid down His life, ___ He rose up a - gain. ___ To us He gives un-end - ing life.
4. Ho - ly, ho - ly the Lord God al - mighty Who was, ___ Who is, ___ and Who is to come. In glo - ry come, Lord Je - sus, come.

15. I surrender all
(medley)

I just want to praise You: A Tannous.
You are the mighty King: Eddie Espinosa.

Winfield S. Weeden
Judson W. Van de Venter
Arr. Christopher Norton

♩ = 76

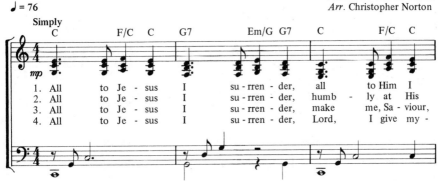

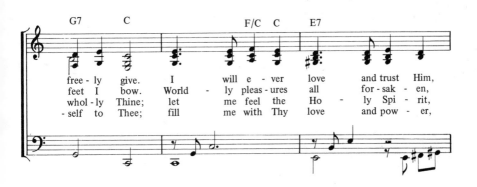

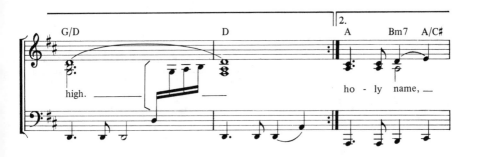

high. _____ ho - ly name, __

I _____ ex - alt Your ho - ly name, __ I _____ ex - alt Your

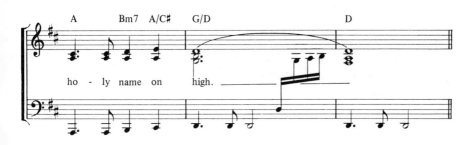

ho - ly name on high. _____

1. And I praise Your name, and I praise Your

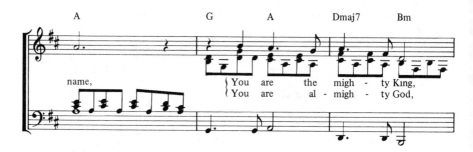

16. I want to praise You, Lord

♩ = 69

Sam O. Scott *and* Randy Thomas

Gently rhythmic
Descant during repeat only

Birds in the sky_ sing their song to You._

mf

I want to love_ serve_ You, Lord, _ much more than I do._ I want to
praise_

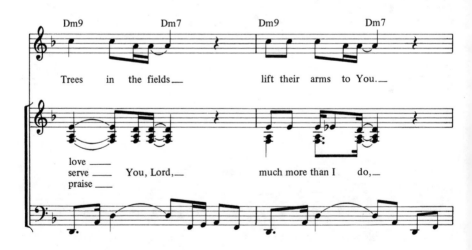

Trees in the fields_ lift their arms to You._

love_ serve_ You, Lord,_ much more than I do,_
praise_

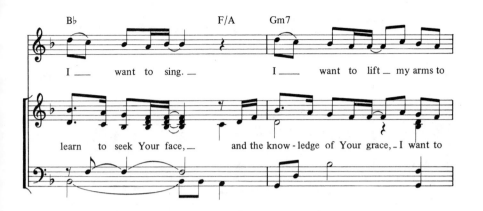

I __ want to sing. __   I __ want to lift __ my arms to

learn   to seek Your face, __   and the know - ledge of Your grace, _ I want to

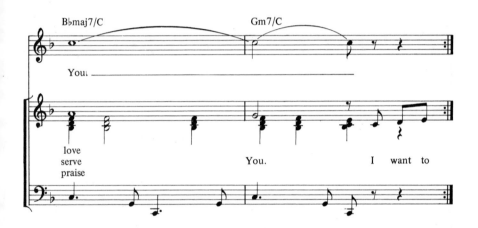

You __

love
serve   You.   I   want to
praise

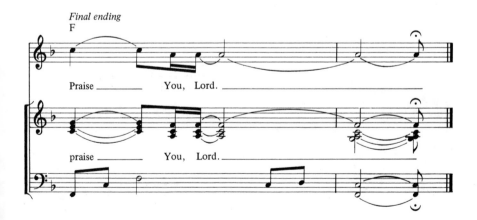

Final ending

Praise _____ You, Lord. _____

praise _____ You, Lord. _____

17. I will praise You, oh Lord

Marlene Wilks
Arr. Roland Fudge

18. Jesus Christ is risen

Frederick Parsonage
Arr. Christopher Norton

♩ = 144

Joyfully

1. Je - sus Christ __ is ri - sen, All - e - lu - ia, what a won-der-ful, hap-py day! Je - sus lives __ for ev - er, All - e - lu - ia, Christ-ians ev-ery-where, join with us and Son.
2. Je - sus Christ __ the Sa - viour, All - e - lu - ia, has this day __ the vict-'ry won. He has con - quered death, sing 'All - e - lu - ia,' one and all __ sing prai - ses to the day.
3. Tell the whole __ wide world, ___ All - e - lu - ia, send the mes - sage far on its way, Je - sus Christ __ is ri - sen, All - e - lu - ia, Christ-ians ce - le - brate this great Eas - ter

Last verse

Lord.

4. Alleluia! Alleluia!
   Alleluia to our Lord!
   Let the world sing 'Alleluia,'
   Alleluia to the Son, our Lord.

19. Just as I am, Lord
(medley)

Come into His presence: unknown.

Jeanne Harper

am, Lord, ___ I wor-ship You, ___ just as I

am, Lord, ___ I come to You. You are so

1. strong, Lord, ___ Your words so true, ___ just as I
2. ten - der, ___ Your love breaks through. ___

am, Lord, I wor - ship You. ___ 2. Just as I

Other verses may be added e.g. Worthy the Lamb, Glory to God, We'll be like Him, etc.

20. Man of sorrows

♩ = 96

P. Bliss (1835-1876)
Arr. Roland Fudge

With breadth

mf 1. Man of so - rrows,
p 2. Mocked by in - sults
p 3. Guilt - y, help - less,

what a name for the Son of God, Who came
harsh and crude, in my place con - demned He stood,
lost were we, blame - less Lamb of God was He,

broadly

ru - ined si - nners to re - claim,
sealed my par - don with His blood,
sa - cri - ficed to set us free,
All - e - lu - ia, what a Sa - viour!

Verse 4: He was lifted up to die,
'It is finished' was His cry,
now in Heav'n exalted high,
alleluia, what a Saviour!

21. Praise song

John Wimber

♩ = 84

With sensitivity and meaning

With pedal throughout ⌐ Ped. ⌐

Son of God, this is our { praise / love } song, Je - sus my Lord, I sing to You. Come now, Spir - it of God, breathe life in-

22. Praise the Lord
(Song of bells)

♩. = 66

Bob Fraser
Arr. Christopher Norton

With a swing

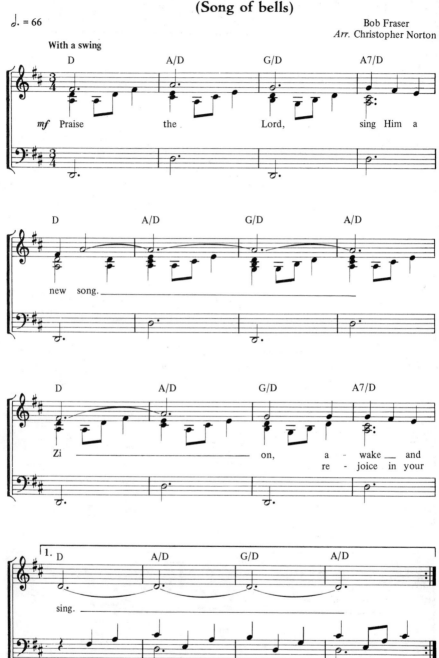

mf Praise the Lord, sing Him a

new song.

Zi - on, a - wake and re - joice in your

sing.

Accompany with bells.

23. Prepare the way

♩ = 120

Mary Smail *and* Colin Green
Arr. Jeanne Harper

With spirit

1. *mf* Pre - pare the way of the Lord,— make His paths straight,—
Refrain fill the earth with the sound of His praise,— Je - sus is Lord, — let
2. come to us as He came — be - fore,— clothed in His grace — to
3. *f* God's King- dom will — in - crease— to fill all the earth — and

op - en the gates — that He may en - ter free - ly
Him be a - dored, — yes, we will have this Man to
stand in our place — and we be - hold Him now, our
show forth His worth;— then right - eous - ness will win, all

Last time to Coda ⊕

in - to our lives,— Ho - san - na we cry — to the
reign o - ver us, — Ho - san - na we fol - low the
Priest and our King,— Ho - san - na we sing — to the
wick - ed - ness cease,— Ho - san - na we wor - ship the

⊕*CODA (Last time only)*

Lord *(Refr.)* and we will
Lord 2. and He will
Lord *(Refr.)* and we will
Lord. 3. You know that - san - na we follow the Lord.
Lord *(Refr.)* and we will

24. Hosanna

♩ = 144

Carl Tuttle
Arr. Christopher Norton

Brightly

Ho - sa - nna, ho - sa - nna, ho - sa-nna in the high - est. Ho - sa - nna, ho - sa - nna, ho - sa-nna in the high - est.

Lord, we lift up Your name, ___

SONGIFTS

2

Songs of Love for the Lord, His Church and World

25. Abba Father

Michael Hudson
Arr. Christopher Norton

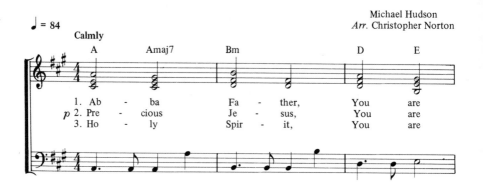

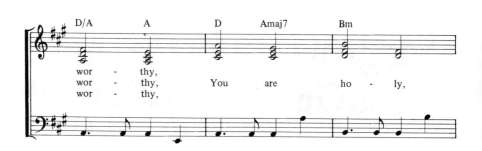

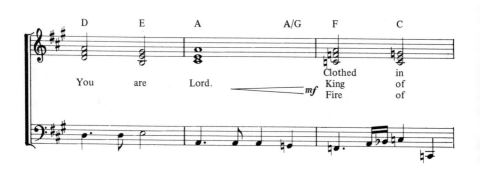

26. Alleluia

Roland Fudge

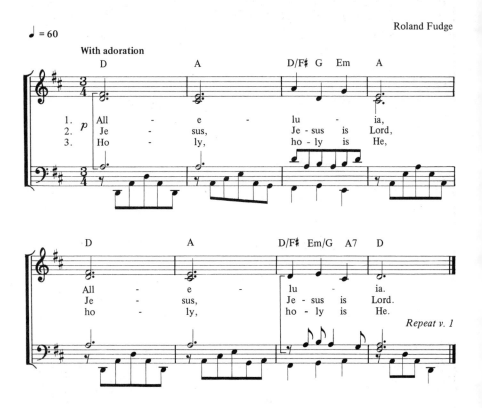

♩ = 60

With adoration

D   A   D/F♯   G   Em   A

1. All - e - lu - ia,
2. Je - sus, Je - sus is Lord,
3. Ho - ly, ho - ly is He,

D   A   D/F♯   Em/G   A7   D

All - e - lu - ia.
Je - sus, Je - sus is Lord.
ho - ly, ho - ly is He.

Repeat v. 1

27. Alleluia

Carl Tuttle
Arr. James Gabriel Stipech

♩ = 72

With quiet adoration

D   G/D   D   G

mp

1. All - e - lu
2. All - e - lu
3. I wor - ship

28. All that I can do

Ted Sandquist
Arr. Jeanne Harper

♩ = 72

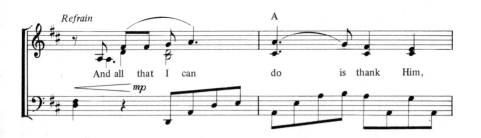

Refrain

And all that I can do is thank Him,

all that I can do is pray,

all that I can do is lift my

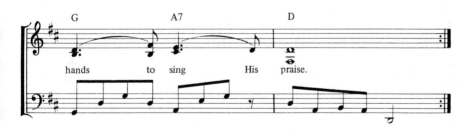

hands to sing His praise.

29. All the earth shall worship

♩ = 72

With awe

Carl Tuttle
Arr. James Gabriel Stipech

1. Fa - ther, ___ we a - dore ___ You, You've
2. Je - sus, ___ we love ___ You, be -
3. Spir - it, ___ we need ___ You to

drawn us to this place. We
cause You first loved us. You
lift us from this mire. Con -

bow down be - fore ___ You,
reached out and healed ___ us
sume and em - pow'r ___ us

hum - bly on our face.
with Your migh - ty touch.
with Your ho - ly fire.

30. Christ is the hope of the world

♩ = 120

Anne-Mari Kaskinen
Arr. Jeanne Harper

With vigour

1. World of trou-ble, world of trau-ma, men sick at heart,—
Christ has come in-to the world, His free-dom He gives,—
2. When we pray and do our work, the Lord does His part,—
ev-en though we of-ten fail, our faith is not strong.—

1. all Cre-at-ion's waiting for a new day to start;— we are called to go and share that
2. all our work bears fruit when God has opened a heart;— Jesus Christ will walk beside us

Chorus

Je-sus Christ lives.— Christ is the hope of the world.—
all the day long.— Christ is the hope of the world.—

It's the mess-age that we bring,
It's the rea-son why we sing.

Verse 3.   Christ, the Lord has come to bring
the whole world to light,
equal are all nations in our loving
God's sight.
Far away in distant lands and
right by our side,
there is always someone for
whom Jesus has died.

Christ is the hope . . .

31. Closer to Thee

32. Father, You are everything to me

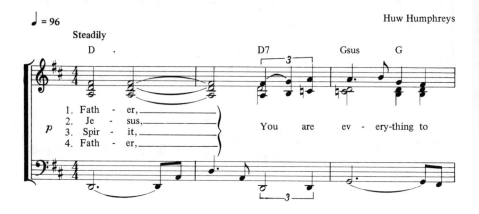

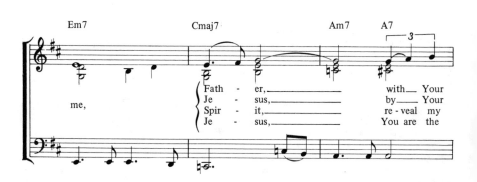

through___ Your heart I long to feel what You
in _____ my life I long to be what You
help_____ me wor - ship and a - dore, Liv - ing
bring_____ our hearts to God as one to wor - ship

feel,_____ what You feel,_____
are,_____ what You are, _____
Lord,_____ Liv - ing Lord,_____
Him,_____ to wor - ship Him, _____

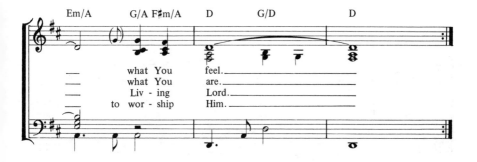

___ what You feel._____
___ what You are._____
___ Liv - ing Lord._____
___ to wor - ship Him. _____

33. Glory and honour to the living Lord

He   a - lone is   wor - thy,   He's the Lord   of
He   a - lone is   wor - thy,   He's the Lord   of

hosts,   all   praise to the Fath   -   er, the
hosts,   all   praise to the Fath   -   er, the

Son and hol - y   Ghost.
Son and hol - y

Ghost.

34. Glory, hallelujah

Mark Pendergrass
Arr. Christopher Norton

35. Holy ground

Christopher Beatty

♩ = 84

With quiet reverence

1. This is ho-ly ground, you're stand-ing on ___ ho-ly ground;
2. This is ho-ly time, He's gi-ven us this ho-ly time;
3. These are ho-ly hands, He's gi-ven us these ho-ly hands;
4. These are ho-ly lips He's gi-ven us ___ ho-ly lips;

for the Lord is pre-sent and where He is, ___ is ho-ly; ___
for all time is His ___ and so this time ___ is ho-ly; ___
He works through these hands ___ and so these hands ___ are ho-ly; ___
He speaks through these lips ___ and so these lips ___ are ho-ly; ___

this is ho-ly ground, you're stand-ing on ___ ho-ly ground;
this is ho-ly time, He's gi-ven us this ho-ly time;
these are ho-ly hands, He's gi-ven us these ho-ly hands;
these are ho-ly lips, He's gi-ven us ___ ho-ly lips;

for the Lord is pre-sent and where He is ___ is ho-ly. ___
for all time is His ___ and so this time ___ is ho-ly. ___
He works through these hands ___ and so these hands ___ are ho-ly. ___
He speaks through these lips ___ and so these lips ___ are ho-ly. ___

Verse 5. These are holy eyes,
He's given us holy eyes,
He sees through these eyes
and so these eyes are holy.
(Repeat)

Verse 6. These are holy ears,
He's given us holy ears,
He speaks to these ears
and so these ears are holy.

36. Holy is the Lord

Brian L. Beshears
Arr. James Gabriel Stipech

37. I bless You, Lord

Carl Tuttle
Arr. James Gabriel Stipech

I bless You, Lord,_____ I bless You, Lord,
I thank You, Lord,_____ I thank You, Lord,
I wor - ship You,_____ I wor - ship You,

bless You, Lord, I bless You, Lord, I
thank You, Lord, I thank You, Lord, I
wor - ship You, I wor - ship You, I

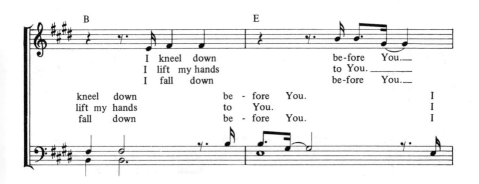

I kneel down be-fore You.____
I lift my hands to You._____
I fall down be-fore You.____

kneel down be - fore You. I
lift my hands to You. I
fall down be - fore You. I

heart, with all of_ my_ mind,

with all of_ my mind,

unison: with all that is with-

in me,_

women: I off-er up _

men: I off-er up_

unison: a sac-ri-fice of

1.2.

praise.

3.

praise.

women: I off-er up_

men: I off-er up_

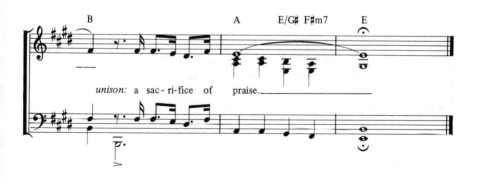

unison: a sac-ri-fice of praise._

38. I sing a new song

Carl Tuttle and John Wimber
Arr. James Gabriel Stipech

♩ = 76

Smoothly

mp 1. I sing a new song to the

Lord, my God. I lift my

voice to Je - sus, the King. And I

wor - ship You, I wor - ship

39. I worship You

Carl Tuttle
Arr. James Gabriel Stipech

40. In moments like these

David Graham
Arr. Christopher Norton

41. Isn't He?

John Wimber
Arr. Christopher Norton

42. Jesus, name above all names
(medley)

He's the Prince of peace: Jim and Anne Mills

Naida Hearn
Arr. Roland Fudge

♪ = 112 Flowing

43. Jesus, we enthrone You

Paul Kyle
Descant and Arr. Roland Fudge

gradually increase intensity until the close.

44. Let our praise to You be as incense

Arr. Christopher Norton

As we see You in Your splen-dour, as we
gaze up-on Your maj-es-ty; as we join the hosts of
an - gels, and pro - claim to - geth - er Your
ho - li - ness. Let our

*Repeat last line ad lib. increasing
then decreasing in intensity.*

Ho - ly, ho-ly, ho - ly, ho - ly is the Lord!

45. Lights to the world

J. Daniels/P. Thompson
Arr. Christopher Norton

Verse 4. Oh burn in us that we may burn,
with love that triumphs in despair.
And touch our lives with such a fire,
that souls may search and find You there.

46. The Lord God most high

Carl Tuttle
Arr. Steven Wray

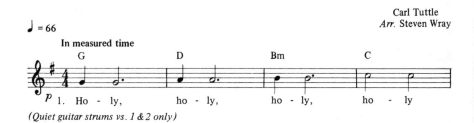

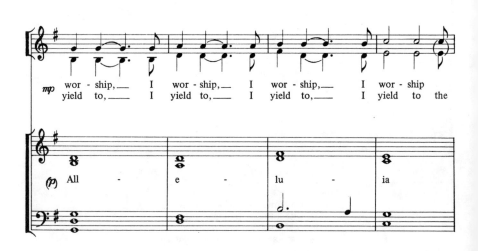

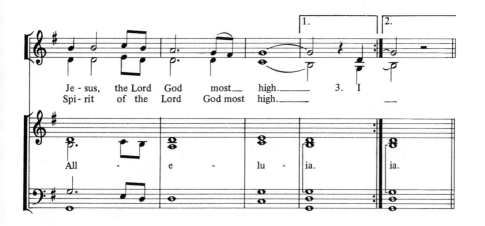

Je - sus, the Lord God most__ high._____ 3. I
Spi - rit of the Lord God most high._____

All - e - lu - ia. ia.

4. Might - y, might - y, might - y, might - y,

5. Wor - thy, wor - thy, wor - thy, wor - thy,

6. Ho - ly, ho - ly, ho - ly, ho - ly,

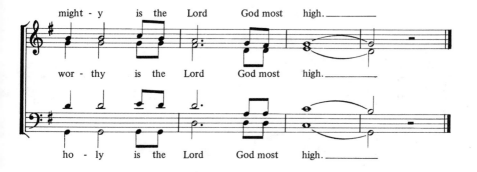

might - y is the Lord God most high._____

wor - thy is the Lord God most high._____

ho - ly is the Lord God most high._____

47. Lord I'll seek after You

Eddie Espinosa
Arr. Ed Cook

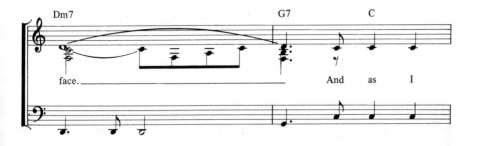

face. _____ And as I

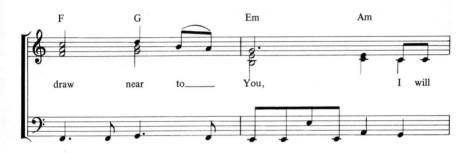

draw near to____ You, I will

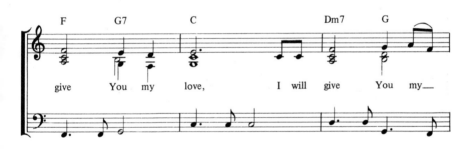

give You my love, I will give You my__

self, I will give You my life.

48. Lord, we praise You
(medley)

This our song: Traditional
Precious Lamb: Traditional

Otis Skillings
Arr. Jeanne Harper

♩ = 80

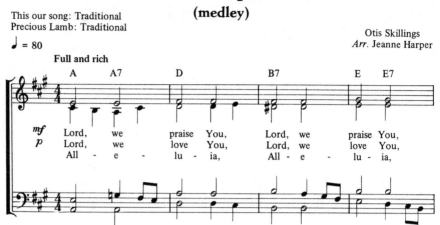

Lord, we praise You, Lord, we praise You,
Lord, we love You, Lord, we love You,
All - e - lu - ia, All - e - lu - ia,

Lord, we praise You, we praise You, Lord.
Lord, we love You, we love You, Lord.
All - e - lu - ia, All - e - lu - ia.*

This our {song / gift} we bring to Thee, {joy - ful / ho - ly} offer - ing

* Optional extra verses: Lord, You love us/me.

may it be, giv - ing plea - sure, Lord, to Thee,

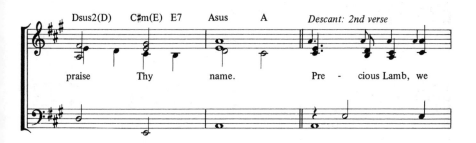

praise Thy name. Pre - cious Lamb, we

Descant: 2nd verse

{praise / love} You, You Who gave Your life for us,

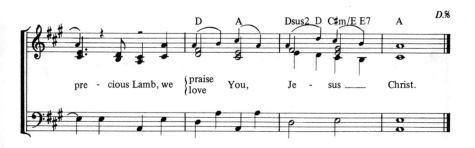

pre - cious Lamb, we {praise / love} You, Je - sus ___ Christ.

49. Most of all

Eddie Espinosa
Arr. James Gabriel Stipech

50. Neighbours

Ghana Folk song
Tom Colvin
Arr. Christopher Norton

Descant last refrain only

♩. = 60 **With a gentle lilt**

Descant: last refrain only

mp Je - su,____ Je - su,____ fill us with Your love, show

us how to serve the neigh-bours we have from You. *Fine*

1. Kneels at the feet of His friends, sil - ent - ly wash - es their
2. Neigh-bours are rich folk and poor, neigh-bours are black, brown and
3. These are the ones we should serve, these are the ones we should
4. Lov - ing puts us on our knees, serv - ing as though we were

feet, mast -er who acts as a slave_ to them._
white, neigh-bours are near - by and far_ a - way._
love, all these are neigh-bours to us_ and You._ Jes -
slaves, this is the way we should live_ with You._

Refrain:

Copyright © 1969 Hope Publishing Co., Carol Stream, IL 60188, U.S.A.
Arr. Copyright © 1986 Ears & Eyes Music, Box TR3, Leeds, LS12 2PN.

51. Neighbours are just beside you

Shi Qigui
Cao Shengjie *Transl.* Jeanne Harper
Arr. Christopher Norton

♩ = 100

With precision, joyful

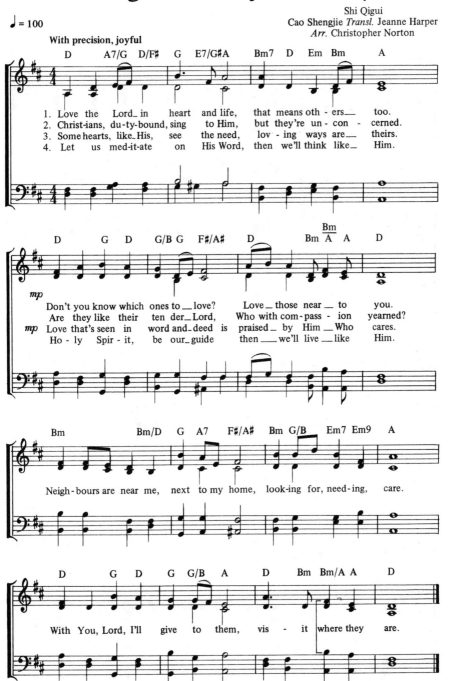

1. Love the Lord in heart and life, that means others too.
2. Christ-ians, du-ty-bound, sing to Him, but they're un-con - cerned.
3. Some hearts, like His, see the need, lov - ing ways are theirs.
4. Let us med-it-ate on His Word, then we'll think like Him.

mp
Don't you know which ones to love? Love those near to you.
Are they like their ten der Lord, Who with com-pass - ion yearned?
mp Love that's seen in word and deed is praised by Him Who cares.
Ho - ly Spir - it, be our guide then we'll live like Him.

Neigh-bours are near me, next to my home, look-ing for, need-ing, care.

With You, Lord, I'll give to them, vis - it where they are.

From the New Hymnal '85 © 1985 China Christian Council, 169 Yuan Ming Yuan Road, Shanghai, Republic of China. [This song was written in 1982. The Rev. Shi Qigui is a pastor of Muen Church, Shanghai, and choirmaster.]

52. Now is the time
(medley)

Father God: Jack Hayford
He is here: Steve Stone
Worthy art Thou: D. Richards

Unknown
Arr. Christopher Norton

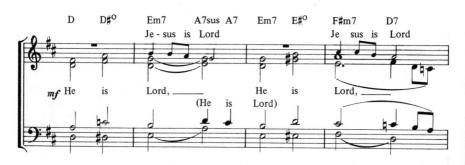

53. One shall tell another

♩ = 108

Graham Kendrick
Arr. Christopher Norton

Lively

mp 1. One shall tell a - no - ther, and he shall tell his
(2.) - pa - ssion of the Fa - ther is rea - dy now to
(3.) longs to do much more than our faith has yet all -

friend, _____ hus - bands, wives and chil - dren shall come
flow, through acts of love and mer - cy, ___
- owed, to thrill us and sur - prise us with His

fo - llow - ing on. From house to house in fam - 'lies shall
we must let it show. He turns now from His an - ger, to
so - vreign power. Where dark - ness has been dar - kest, the

all be ga - thered in, and lights will shine in
show a smi - ling face, and longs that men should
brigh - test light will shine, His in - vi - ta - tion

ev - ery street, so warm and wel - com - ing.
stand be - neath the foun - tain of His grace.
comes to us, it's yours and it is mine.

Chorus

Come on in and taste the new wine,
Here is hea - ling and for - give - ness,

the wine of the king - dom, the wine of the

king - dom of God.

Final chorus

(2. Com-)
(3. He)

54. Send me out from here

♩ = 138

With urgency

John Pantry

Send me out from here, Lord, to serve a world in need, may I know no man by the coat he wears, but the heart that Je-sus sees. ___ And may the light of Your face, Lord, ___ shine up-on me now. You have

Last time
To Coda ✦

filled my heart with the great-est joy and my cup is ov-er-flow-ing.

55. Thank You, Lord, for Your presence here

Guitar: Tune 6th string one tone lower to D

Roland Fudge

♩ = 60

Gently flowing

Thank You, Lord, for Your pre - sence here,
thank You Lord, thank You Lord. Thank You Lord, You re -
move all fear, thank You Lord, thank You Lord. For the
love that You showed as You poured out Your

life, we thank You, we bless You, Christ

Je - sus our Lord, we thank You, Lord.

Thank You, Lord.

Thank You, Lord.

56. Thou art holy
(medley)

Jesus, Thou art holy: Unknown

Gary Johnson
Arr. Jeanne Harper

♩ = 88

In measured time

1. Thou art ho - ly, Thou art ho - ly, dwell - ing in our prais - es, Thou art ho - ly.
2. Thou art wor - thy, Thou art wor - thy, to re - ceive our wor - ship Thou art wor - thy.
3. Al - le - u - ia, all - el - u - ia, all - el - u - ia all - el - u - ia.

Je - sus, Thou art the ho - ly, the ho - ly Son of God, the ho - ly Son of God,
Wor - thy Lamb of God, wor - thy Lamb of God, wor - thy Lamb of God,
Might - y King of kings, might - y King of kings might - y King of kings

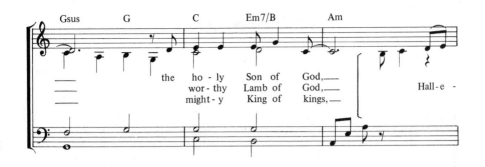

the ho - ly Son of God,   Hall - e -
wor - thy Lamb of God,
might - y King of kings,

lu - jah   to Thy   name,   hall - e -

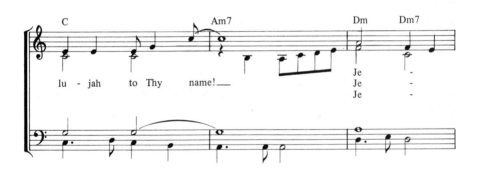

lu - jah   to Thy   name!   Je   -
Je   -
Je   -

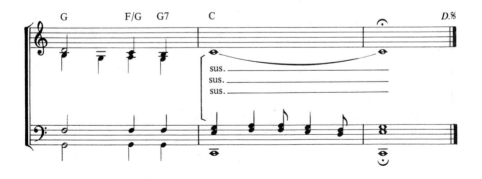

sus.
sus.
sus.

57. Together

John Wimber
Arr. James Gabriel Stipech

we_____ will al - ways be _____ to -

ge - ther, through

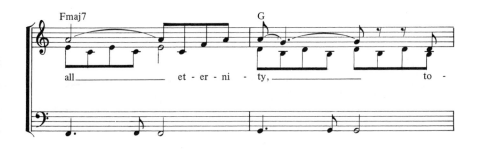

all_____ et - er - ni - ty, _____ to -

ge - ther.

2. Je- sus,
3. Bro-thers

58. Turn the hearts of the children

Jimmy Owens
Arr. Jeanne Harper

59. Within the veil

Ruth Dryden
Arr. Pete Desmond

♩ = 90

With quiet devotion

1. With-in the veil, I long to come,
   veil, my Fath-er dwells

in - to the ho - ly place, to look up - on His face,____
on His et - er - nal throne, His fa - mi - ly to own,____

____ I see such beau - ty there,____ none oth - er can com-pare,____
____ no sin can en - ter there.____ ho - ly He makes me here,____

____ I wor-ship Thee, my God, with-in the veil ____ 2. With-in the ____
____ that like my Lord I'll be

60. Worthy, O worthy are You, Lord

Capo 2(D)

♩ = 80

Mark Kinzer and
Greg Jacob

61. You are the vine

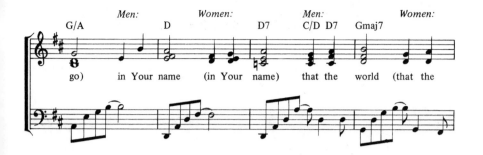

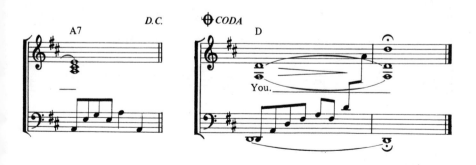

62. Father, make us one

Rick Ridings
Arr. and Descant Christopher Norton

♩ = 92

Prayerfully

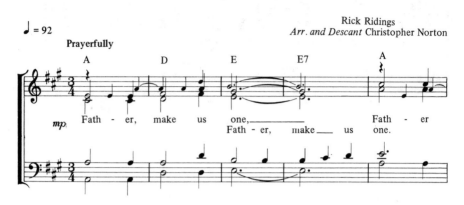

Fath - er, make us one, _____ Fath - er

Fath - er, make __ us one.

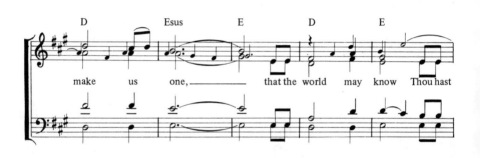

make us one, _____ that the world may know Thou hast

sent the Son, __ Fath - er, make us one. _____

SONGIFTS

3

Songs of Hope and Vision

63. African song

Local Kenyan Melody
M.G. Mutsoli
Arr. Roland Fudge

The use of bongos is suggested.

64. Awake, O Israel

Merla Watson
Arr. Christopher Norton

♩ = 120

Rousing

1. A-wake, O Is - rael, __ put off thy slum - ber, and the truth __ shall set you free, for out of Zi - on __ comes thy De - liv - 'rer, __ in the year of Ju - bi -lee. __ 2. For in the

fur - nace __ of much aff - lic - tion I have cho - sen thee, be - hold, and so for ir - on __ I'll give thee sil - ver __ and for brass I'll give thee gold. __ 3. Thou art My

cho-sen, __ for I have sought __ thee, thou art gra - ven up -on My hand, and I will gath-er __ all those that scat-ter, __ they shall come back to their land. __ 4. Oh, hall-e -

lu - jah, __ oh, hall - e - lu - jah! Hall- e - lu - jah! Oh, praise the Lord! Oh, hall-e - lu- jah, __ oh, hall- e - liv - 'rer, lu - jah, __ hall- e - lu - jah! Praise the Lord!

mf

[Chords: Dm Am7 Dm A7 Dm Dm/F Gm | Dm A A/C♯ Dm Dm/F | Gm Dm/A Am7 Dm A7 (Dm)]

[1,2,3.] **[4.]**

65. The Bridegroom song

♩ = 40 increasing in tempo to ♩ = 96 after several repeats

With strength and joy

John McNeil
Arr. Jeanne Harper

Refrain

Sound on the trum-pet, call to the peo - ple, sing your new___
Break out the ban - ners, join in the danc - ing, no time for___

song. Our Bride - groom's com - ing,
gloom. Pre - pare the ban - quet,

it won't be long.
He's com - ing soon.

Last time *(Shout)*

Yes!

1. If you're___ one of God's
2. Go out___ in tears and

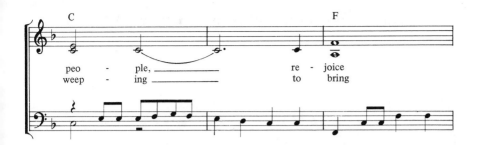

peo - ple, _____ re - joice
weep - ing _____ to bring

in praise and song. _____ Come lift up _____
the har - vest home. _____ It's time for_____

_____ your hearts be - fore Him _____ and give your voi - ces _____
_____ the joy of reap - ing, _____ in joy the sheaves now_____

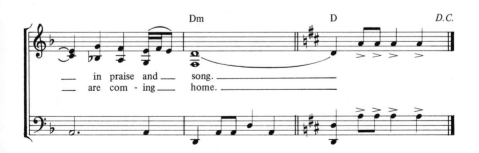

_____ in praise and _____ song. _____
_____ are com - ing _____ home. _____

66. Crown Him with many crowns

G.V. Elvey (1816-1893)
M. Bridges and G. Thring

♩ = 112

Victoriously

1. Crown Him with ma - ny crowns, the Lamb up - on His
2. Crown Him the Lord of life, tri - umph - ant from the
mp 3. Crown Him the Lord of love Who shows His hands and

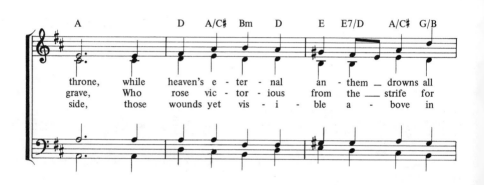

throne, while heaven's e - ter - nal an - them ⌣ drowns all
grave, Who rose vic - tor - ious from the ⌣ strife for
side, those wounds yet vis - i - ble a - bove in

mus - ic but its own! A - wake, my soul, and
those He came to save: His glor - ies now we
beau - ty glor - i - fied. *mp* No an - gel in the

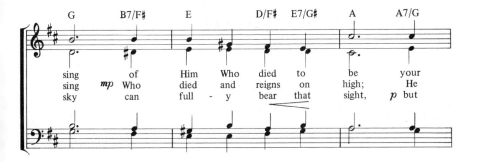

sing of Him Who died to be your
sing *mp* Who died and reigns on high; He
sky can full - y bear that sight, *p* but

Last time
To Coda ⊕

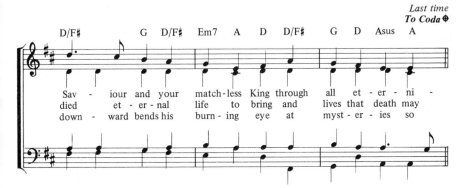

Sav - iour and your match-less King through all et - er - ni -
died et - er - nal life to bring and lives that death may
down - ward bends his burn - ing eye at myst - er - ies so

⊕ *CODA*

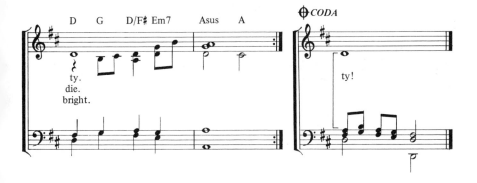

ty.
die.
bright.

ty!

Verse 4. Crown Him the Lord of peace —
His Kingdom is at hand,
from pole to pole let warfare cease
and Christ rule every land!
A city stands on high
His glory it displays
and there the nations 'Holy' cry
in joyful hymns of praise.

Verse 5. Crown Him the Lord of years,
the potentate of time,
Creator of the rolling spheres
in majesty sublime;
all hail, Redeemer, hail,
for You have died for me;
Your praise shall never, never fail
through all eternity!

67. The crowning day

El Nathan
J. McGranahan
Arr. Christopher Norton

♩ = 69

Full and rich

1. Our Lord is now re-ject-ed and by the world dis-owned, by the man-y still ne-glect-ed, and by the few en-throned. But soon He'll come in glo-ry, the hour is draw-ing nigh, for the crown-ing day is com-ing by and by.

2. The heav'ns shall glow with splen-dour, but bright-er far than they, the saints shall shine in glo-ry as Christ shall them ar-ray. The beau-ty of the Sav-iour shall dazz-le ev-'ry eye, in the crown-ing day that's com-ing by and by.

3. Our pain shall then be ov-er, we'll sin and sigh no more, be-hind us all of sor-row and nought but joy be-fore. A joy in our Re-deem-er, as we to Him are nigh, oh the crown-ing day is com-ing by and by. Oh, the

4. Let all that look for, hasten the coming joyful day,
   by earnest consecration to walk the narrow way;
   by gath'ring in the lost ones, for whom our Lord did die,
   for the crowning day that's coming by and by.

   Oh, the crowning day is coming! *etc.*

68. Great is Your faithfulness

W.M. Runyan (1870-1957)
Thomas O. Chisholm
Arr. Roland Fudge

(Descant after Verses 2 and 3)

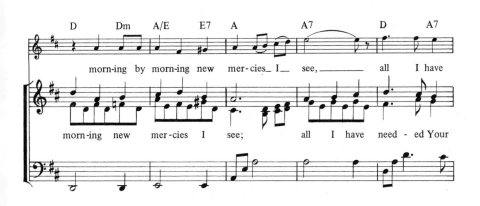

69. He made us to praise Him

70. Holy Lord

Jeanne Harper

Basic speed ♩ = 104
Contemplative

1. Ho - ly is the Lord, _____ ho - ly is the Lord, _____ ho - ly, ho - ly, ho - ly is He;
2. Judge - ment has the Lord, _____ judge - ment has the Lord, _____ judge - ment, judge ment, judge - ment has He;
3. Mer - cy has the Lord, _____ mer - cy has the Lord, _____ mer - cy, mer - cy, mer - cy has He;
4. Like ___ Him I will be, _____ like ___ Him I will be, _____ like ___ Him, like ___ Him, like ___ Him I'll be;

All - e - lu - ia. _____

71. I'll lift my eyes to the hills

Phil Potter
Arr. Christopher Norton

1. I'll lift my eyes to the hills,
2. I'll bring my praise to the Lord,
3. Lift up your voice to the Lord.
4. We lift our hands to the Lord.
5. We lift our hearts to the King.

I'll lift my eyes to the
I'll bring my praise to the
Lift up your voice to the
We lift our hands to the
We lift our hearts to the

hills,
Lord,
Lord,
Lord,
King,

I'll lift my
I'll bring my
lift up your
we lift our
we lift our

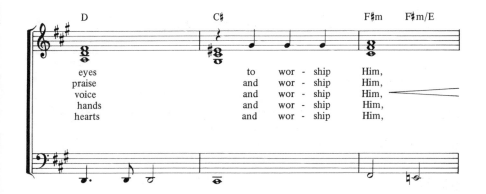

D   C♯   F♯m   F♯m/E

eyes	to	wor - ship	Him,
praise	and	wor - ship	Him,
voice	and	wor - ship	Him,
hands	and	wor - ship	Him,
hearts	and	wor - ship	Him,

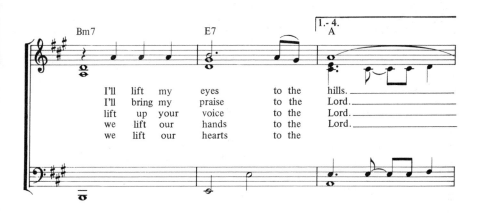

Bm7   E7   1.- 4.   A

I'll	lift	my	eyes	to the	hills.
I'll	bring	my	praise	to the	Lord.
lift	up	your	voice	to the	Lord.
we	lift	our	hands	to the	Lord.
we	lift	our	hearts	to the	

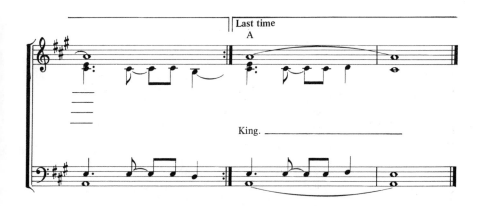

Last time   A

King.

72. Iranian song

Bahram Dehqani
Bishop Hassan Dehqani
Arr. Christopher Norton

With quiet majesty

mf 1. You, oh my God, gifts of know-ledge give to me, that hid-den mys-ter-ies I may clear-ly see. Free me from in-ward fights, life's tang-led skein. My torn heart heal, oh Lord, make me glad a-gain.

Verse 2. Spirit of God, Source of wisdom, guidance, life,
Yet to receive these gifts, we must daily die.
Spirit of Jesus Christ reaches our pain,
Consciences weak through guilt, He'll make whole again.

Verse 3. Love from the human heart through selfishness will fail,
love that Your Spirit gives, causes it to pale.
Lord fill us deep within, so friends will know,
to even enemies, Your love we can show.

Verse 4. Jesus, we'll follow You, servant hearts we need,
with Your compassion, Lord, others we will feed.
Grant us to follow You, never retreat,
gladly to wash and cleanse one another's feet.

Verse 5. People without God are living for themselves,
bringing such sep'rateness, suffering and fear.
Come Lord and show us all Your power can heal,
uproot the source of hate, may Your peace reign here.

Verse 6. You, oh my God, gifts of knowledge give to me
that hidden mysteries I may clearly see.
Living obediently, grace You'll endue,
my soul and character You'll make wholly new.

73. Jesus shall reign where'er the sun

Psalmodia Evangelica 1789
Isaac Watts
Descant Roland Fudge

♩ = 80

With breadth and movement

5. Let all cre - a - tion rise and bring the high-est hon-ours to our__ King;

an-gels de-scend, an-gels de-scend with songs a-gain and earth re-peat the loud__ 'A-men'.

Verse 1. Jesus shall reign where'er the sun
does his successive journeys run;
His kingdom stretch from shore to shore
till moons shall rise and set no more.

Verse 2. People and realms of every tongue
declare His love in sweetest song,
and children's voices shall proclaim
their early blessings on His name.

Verse 3. Blessings abound where Jesus reigns —
the prisoner leaps to lose his chains,
the weary find eternal rest,
the hungry and the poor are blessed.

Verse 4. To Him shall endless prayer be made,
and princes throng to crown His head;
His name like incense shall arise
with every morning sacrifice.

Verse 5. Let all creation rise and bring
the highest honours to our King;
angels descend with songs again
and earth repeat the loud 'Amen'.

74. The kingdom of God

Paul Bateman
Bryn Rees
Arr. Christopher Norton

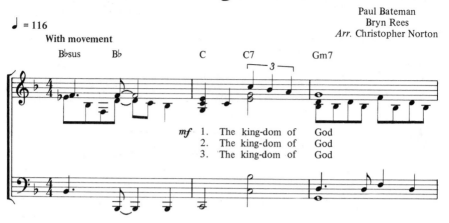

1. The king-dom of God
2. The king-dom of God
3. The king-dom of God

1. is jus - tice and joy, for Je - sus re -
2. is mer - cy and grace, the lep - ers are
3. is chal-lenge and choice, be - lieve the good

1. stores what sin would des - stroy,
2. cleansed, the sin - ners find place,
3. news, re - pent and re - joice!

4. God's kingdom is come,
   the gift and the goal,
   in Jesus begun, in heaven made whole,
   the heirs of the kingdom
   shall answer His call,
   and all things cry 'Glory',
   to God all in all!

75. Lo! He comes

Betty Pulkingham
Charles Wesley

♩ = 76

With majesty

1. Lo! He comes, with clouds de - scend - ing,
2. Ev - 'ry eye shall now be - hold Him,
3. Those dear to - kens of His pas - sion
4. Yea, a - men! Let all a - dore Thee,

once for our sal - va - tion slain; thou - sand, thou-sand
robed in dread - ful maj - es - ty; those who set at
still His dazz - ling bo - dy bears, cause of end - less
high on Thine et - er - nal throne; Sav - iour, take the

saints at - tend - ing swell the tri - umph of His
naught and sold Him, pierced and nail'd Him to the
ex - ul - ta - tion to His ran - som'd wor - ship
power and glo - ry, claim the king - dom for Thine

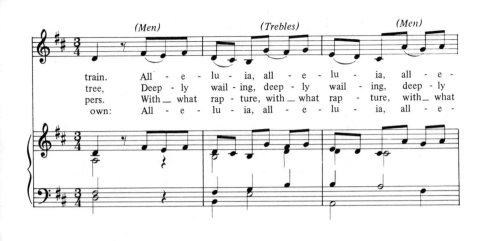

train. All - e - lu - ia, all - e - lu - ia, all - e -
tree, Deep - ly wail-ing, deep-ly wail - ing, deep-ly
pers. With_ what rap - ture, with_ what rap - ture, with_ what
own: All - e - lu - ia, all - e - lu - ia, all - e -

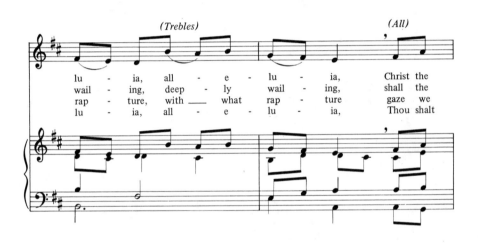

lu - ia, all - e - lu - ia, Christ the
wail - ing, deep - ly wail - ing, shall the
rap - ture, with _ what rap - ture gaze we
lu - ia, all - e - lu - ia, Thou shalt

Lord re - turns _____ to reign.
true Mes - si - ah see.
on those glo - rious scars!
reign, and Thou _____ a - lone.

76. Lord, now speak to us

Peter Sandwall
Lars Mörlid

Basic tempo ♩ = 60

Flowing and with flexibility

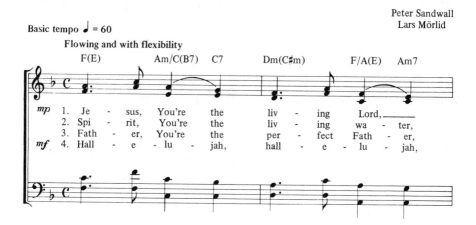

mp
1. Je - sus, You're the liv - ing Lord,___
2. Spi - rit, You're the liv - ing wa - ter,
3. Fath - er, You're the per - fect Fath - er,
mf
4. Hall - e - lu - jah, hall - e - lu - jah,

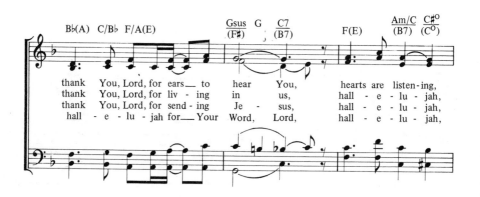

thank You, Lord, for ears__ to hear You, hearts are listen-ing,
thank You, Lord, for liv - ing in us, hall - e - lu - jah,
thank You, Lord, for send - ing Je - sus, hall - e - lu - jah,
hall - e - lu - jah for__ Your Word, Lord, hall - e - lu - jah,

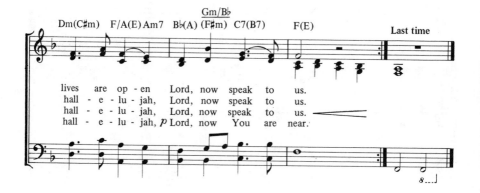

lives are op - en Lord, now speak to us.
hall - e - lu - jah, Lord, now speak to us.
hall - e - lu - jah, Lord, now speak to us.___
hall - e - lu - jah, p Lord, now You are near.

77. Christ the everlasting Lord

Hong Luming
Shen Yifan *Transl.* Jeanne Harper
Arr. Christopher Norton

♩ = 100
Simply

mp

1. Have you ev - er____ known what there was when
2. Oh, how deep is His love, God be - came a
3. Let us now re - spond, seek the One Whose

time be - gan? God was there, with His pre - cious Son,
man like____ us. His - t'ry knew its Rul - er di - vine,
word is His bond. Jes - us shows us what He is like,

mak - ing all things by Their____ word, keep-ing all things is our
ov - er all sal - va - tion could shine! Vic - to - ry is for all
ov - er - whelms us with His____ life. Al - pha and O - meg - a,

God, Christ the ev - er - last - ing Lord!
time, Christ the ev - er - last - ing Lord!
He! Christ the ev - er - last - ing Lord!

78. My God, how wonderful You are

J. Turle
F.W. Faber
Arr. Roland Fudge

♩ = 84

With reverence and awe

1. My God, how won-der-ful You are, Your maj - es - ty how bright; how beau - ti - ful Your mer - cy - seat in depths of burn-ing light.
2. Cre - a - tor from et - er - nal years, and ev - er - last-ing Lord, by ho - ly an-gels day and night in - cess - ant - ly ad - ored.
3. How won-der-ful, how beau-ti - ful the sight of You must be, Your end-less wis-dom, bound-less power and awe - ful pur-i - ty.

4. O how I fear You, living God
with deepest tenderest fears,
and worship You with trembling hope
and penitential tears!

5. But I may love too, O Lord,
though You are all-divine,
for You have stooped to ask of me
this feeble love of mine.

6. Father of Jesus, love's reward,
great King upon Your throne,
what joy to see You as You are
and know as I am known!

79. Open your eyes

Carl Tuttle
Arr. Ed Cook

80. Revive Your work, Lord

Jeanne Harper

♩ = 112

With strength

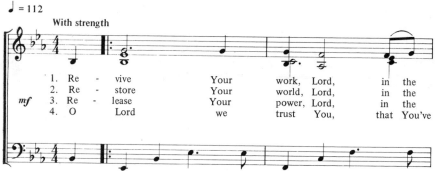

1. Re - vive Your work, Lord, in the
2. Re - store Your world, Lord, in the
mf 3. Re - lease Your power, Lord, in the
4. O Lord we trust You, that You've

midst of the years for__ You are our
midst of the years for__ You have pro-
midst of the years in__ signs and in
heard now our prayer, oh__ work in our

Head, You are Lord__ of Your Church; there's
claimed it is like a fa - ded cloth; the
won - ders that no - one can ig - nore; all
hearts that we care and long like You, but

none whose will can hin - der Your
day is soon when You'll bring the
men will see when You move in
now we'll praise You, wait on Your

power, You will choose Your mo - ment then Your pre - sence
new. Let us see with eyes of faith the things that
power, they will watch Your Church and then they'll fear, or
will, for You'll use us in Your might - y plan our

1-3. **Last time**

will ap - pear.
God will do.
they'll a - dore.
prayer ful - - fil.

81. We are citizens of heaven

Costis Papazoglou
Arr. Christopher Norton

1. Ci - ti - zens of heav'n, seat - ed with our Lord a - bove, we're
2. Child - ren of our Fath - er, we now en - joy His peace, while
3. Mes - sen - gers of Je - sus, we shout out our good news. Our

mem - bers of His Bo - dy, un - it - ed in His love. By
oth - ers are so des - perate, they long for pain to cease. But
lov - ing Lord is want - ing not one His gift should lose. By

work-ing on and fight-ing on, _____ we'll give glo - ry to __ our
pray-ing, thank-ing, prais-ing Him, _____ He'll per - fect in us __ His
win-ning, build-ing, go-ing out, _____ we'll ful - fil our Mas - ter's

God. And He's now our Guide each step of the
joy. And when Sa -tan tries to come, we are
plan. We'll tell oth - ers of His cross, re - con -

SONGIFTS

4

Songs of Encouragement

82. The armour of God

Capo 1(A)

Anne *and* Andrew Barton

♩ = 80

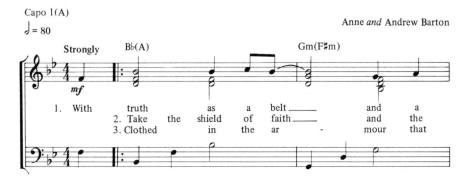

1. With truth as a belt and a
2. Take the shield of faith and the
3. Clothed in the ar - mour that

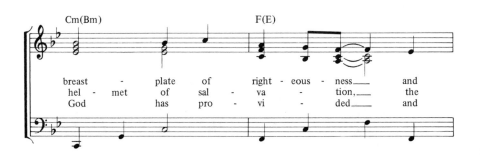

breast - plate of right - eous - ness and
hel - met of sal - va - tion, the
God has pro - vi - ded and

feet that are shod with the gos - pel of
sword of the Spi - rit which is the word of
then you will stand till the vic - t'ry is

peace, be strong in the Lord, in the
God, be
won, so be

strength of His might and put on the whole ar-

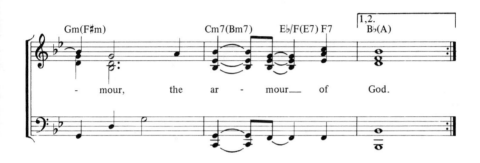

-mour, the ar - mour of God.

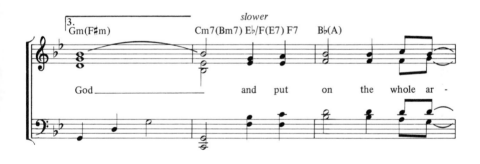

God and put on the whole ar-

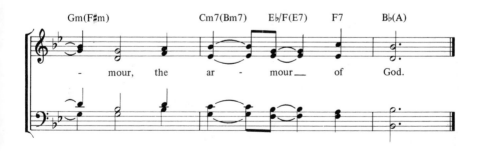

-mour, the ar - mour of God.

83. Another day of victory

Ruth Fazal
Arr. Christopher Norton

♩ = 144

Brightly

1. An - oth - er day __ of vic - to - ry __ in Je - sus, __
lieve we have __ the vic - to - ry __ in Je - sus, __

an - oth - er day __ of vic - to - ry __ in
be - lieve we have __ the vic - to - ry __ in

Him, __ oh __ Lord, send us out in
Him, __ oh __ Lord, You have sent us

Your name we pray and __ give us __ the
out in Your name You have giv'n us __ the

vic - to - ry __ to - day. __ 2. Be -
vic - to - ry __ to - day.

84. The battle belongs to the Lord

Jamie Owens-Collins
Arr. Christopher Norton

85. Be lifted up, my soul

Unknown
Arr. Jeanne Harper

Lord. The Lord is gra - cious and mer - ci - ful, __ He's
So put your hand in His hand each day, __ show

slow to an - ger and swift to bless, be lift - ed
Him your heart, He'll show you the way, be lift - ed

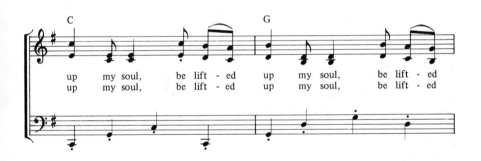

up my soul, be lift - ed up my soul, be lift - ed
up my soul, be lift - ed up my soul, be lift - ed

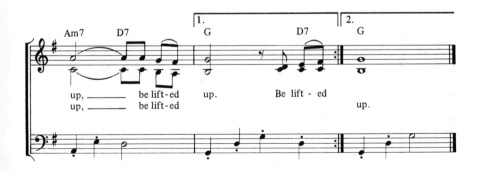

up, _____ be lift-ed up. Be lift - ed
up, _____ be lift-ed up.

86. By faith in His strength

Capo 3 (D)

Christopher Norton
Jeanne Harper

♩ = 112

Stirring

1. By faith in His strength we are told to __ be strong; with - in and with - out, __ God's work needs to be done. Both blessed with His Spi - rit, for -
2. 'Put on now My arm - our, pro - tect - ed __ you'll be; in life's dai - ly __ pres - sure, work from fear you'll be free; re - mem - ber, by dear Lord knew faith you take
3. Though Sa - tan should har - ass you to weak - en __ your trust, the Word stands be - fore __ you, be - lieve it you must! Like us, our dear Lord knew temp -

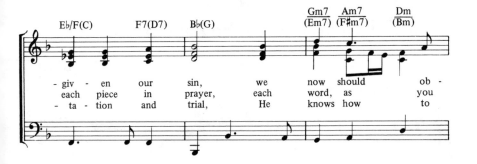

	Eb/F(C)	F7(D7)	Bb(G)		Gm7 (Em7)	Am7 (F#m7)	Dm (Bm)

- giv - en our sin, we now should ob -
each piece in prayer, each word, as you
- ta - tion and trial, He knows how to

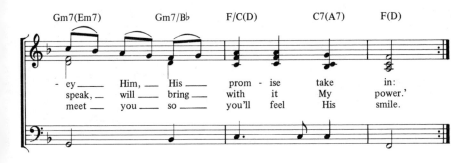

Gm7(Em7)		Gm7/Bb	F/C(D)		C7(A7)	F(D)

- ey____ Him, ___ His ____ prom - ise take in:
speak, __ will ____ bring ___ with it My power.'
meet ___ you __ so ____ you'll feel His smile.

4. Now take your authority, rejoice in the Name;
   Its power is for eternity, for ever the same.
   Depend on His Spirit, His wisdom you need
   To choose God's way only, from others be freed.

5. Link with your new family, together seek Him.
   The time is so very short, His lost world to win.
   Receive one another and you will be strong
   to tread on your enemy while walking along.

6. So tasting the power of the ages to come,
   learn now what it's like to have heaven as home,
   for nearer today than when first you believed,
   is your own salvation,– for you'll be received!

87. Come see the beauty of the Lord

Graham Kendrick

* This song is sung as a call and response throughout, the congregation copying the leader or the ladies following the men.

88. Crown of glory

Ruth Fazal
Michael Harper
Arr. Christopher Norton

♩ = 63

Thoughtfully

1. Oh My child-ren, I am want-ing you to see ___ the cost of My call to u - ni - ty. ___
call - ing you to hum - ble your - selves, ___ not on - ly to Me, but to each oth-er. ___
call - ing you to be ___ in the world ___ a light and a lea - ven to all peo-ple. ___
prais - es are not pleas - ing to Me, ___ for your hearts are dis - o - be - dient and ___ stub-born. ___
child-ren, look to Je - sus, your Sav-iour ___ so hum - ble and lov - ing and for - giv-ing. ___

It is not an ea-sy road to go a - long, ___ for the sha-dow of My cross lies on that way. ___
Re - frain from the ac - cu - sing of your bro-ther, ___ for My peo - ple this is grie - ving un-to Me. ___
But I'm grieved at how you cut each oth - er down, ___ and I'm grieved ___ at the hard - ness of your hearts. ___
All the off - 'rings that you bring Me, they mean no - thing, ___ for you will not let your lives be ruled by Me. ___
Are you rea - dy now to go this way I'm call-ing, ___ be o - be - dient un - to Me, so I can bless you? ___

89. Fear not, for I have redeemed you

90. The fear of the Lord

Basic tempo ♩ = 72
Freely

Jeanne Harper

mp
1. If you ask of Me, when you cry to Me, I will
℞ ask of Me, as you seek My face, I will
2. I will ask of You, I will cry to You, and You'll
℞ ask of You, I will seek Your face, and You'll

(end of vs. 1, 2 to ⊕)

put _____ My fear on you. When you
put _____ _____ My fear on
put _____ Your fear on me. I will
put _____ _____ Your fear on

you. Then you will know _____ I am a ho - ly God,
me. Then I will know _____ You are a ho - ly God,

Fine

then you will know _____ Who I am. _____ When you
then I will know _____ Who You are. _____ I will

mf

D.℞.

This song may be followed by 'Holy ground' No. 35

91. The coconut woman

♩ = 120

With a swing

Harry Belafonte *and* Lord Burgess

A Caribbean song, usually accompanied by bongos, maracas, and tambourines

92. God can do it again

♩ = 84 *(verses)*
♩ = 104 *(refrain)*
Lively

Donald Moen
Optional vs. 3, 4 and *arr.* Jeanne Harper

1. Time af-ter time I hear peo-ple say to me
2. You've asked God to meet your need, so why not trust in Him?
mf *(3. And) what now of the world He loves? He is its Lord and King. He's
*4. Many don't have eyes of faith, they think that ev-il reigns. They

"Why don't we see mir-ac-les like there used to be?" Well I
God has done it all be-fore, He'll do it all a-gain. He's
watch-ing and He's work-ing out His will in ev-'ry-thing. ___
don't see there's a King su-preme, Who laughs at Sa-tan's aims. But

still be-lieve in mir-a-cles, God hears us when we pray; 'twas
will-ing, much more will-ing ___ than I could ev-er say, to
Tam-ing and sub-du-ing ___ the re-bel heart of man, ___
soon there'll be a glo-rious day, the hid-den will be seen; we'll

* Optional verse.

93. Golgotha

Paavo Virtanen
Transl. and arr. Jeanne Harper

♩ = 92

With depth and reverence

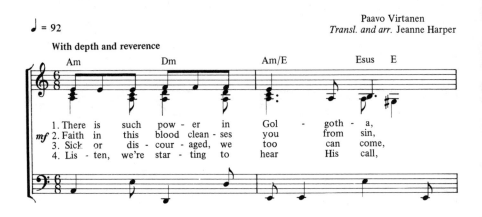

1. There is such pow - er in Gol - goth - a,
mf 2. Faith in this blood clean - ses you from sin,
3. Sick or dis - cour - aged, we too can come,
4. Lis - ten, we're star - ting to hear His call,

pow'r in the blood that's be - yond com - pare.
blood that re - news us all deep with - in.
Je - sus re - stores and says "Wel - come home."
trum - pet - blast soon on our ears will fall.

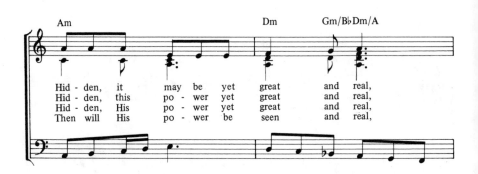

Hid - den, it may be yet great and real,
Hid - den, this po - wer yet great and real,
Hid - den, His po - wer yet great and real,
Then will His po - wer be seen and real,

v1-3 Ev - 'ry - where, al - ways, we all can feel
v4 Ev - 'ry - where, ev - 'ry - one then will feel

v1-4 there is such pow - er in Gol - goth - a,

mp

pow'r in the blood that's be - yond____ com - pare.

94. Gracious God, our Father

Zhao Baoheng *and* Zhao Shaoyun
Transl. Jeanne Harper
Arr. Christopher Norton

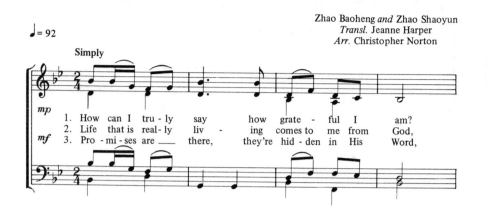

1. How can I tru-ly say how grate-ful I am?
2. Life that is real-ly liv-ing comes to me from God,
3. Pro-mi-ses are ___ there, they're hid-den in His Word,

God___ is my lov-ing, heav'n-ly Fa - ther.
turn-ing fears and wor-ries in-to trust - ing.
ma-ny diff-'rent pro-mi-ses for all His Church.

He___ knows my weak - ness, He___ knows my pains,
Trou-bles turn to peace, an - xi-e-ties to joy,
Ask and you'll re-ceive, then seek and you shall find,

From the New Hymnal '85. Copyright © 1985 China Christian Council, 169 Yuan Ming Yuan Road, Shanghai, Republic of China. This song was written in 1981. Zhao Shaoyun is an eighty-year-old Elder of his church in central China. Baoheng is his son.

day by day He com-forts, guides and cares for me.
from con-fu-sion He leads in-to clar - i - ty.
if you knock, the door will sure-ly o - pen.

And there's more than this, He's pre-par-ing
Hall - e - lu - jah! Hall - e - lu -
Know that you need faith, know that God will

me, step by step I'm near - ing heav'n with
jah! Through my gra - cious Fa - ther I am
hear, you will be sur - prised to have such

Him. Glo - ry to our God!
blessed.
peace.

To be accompanied with quiet tuned percussion and viola if available.

95. However loud the shout

Ian Sharp
Elizabeth Cosnett

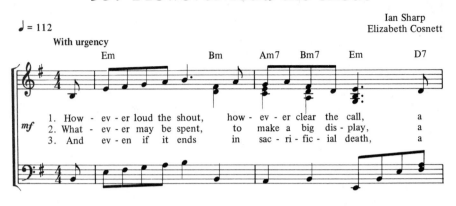

1. How - ev - er loud the shout, how - ev - er clear the call, a
2. What - ev - er may be spent, to make a big dis - play, a
3. And ev - en if it ends in sac - ri - fic - ial death, a

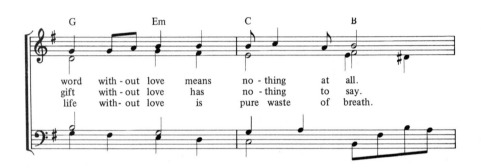

word with - out love means no - thing at all.
gift with - out love has no - thing to say.
life with - out love is pure waste of breath.

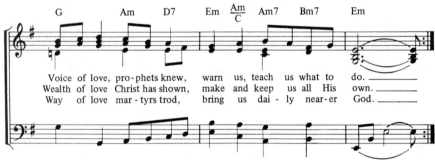

Voice of love, pro - phets knew, warn us, teach us what to do. _____
Wealth of love Christ has shown, make and keep us all His own. _____
Way of love mar - tyrs trod, bring us dai - ly near - er God. _____

4. However sound the plans,
   and clever the ideas,
   a world without love
   is ashes and tears.

God of love
Christ displayed
claim the conquest
You have made.

This is one of the prize-winning hymns of the BBC 1982 hymn competition.

96. Jesus is Lord of all

Marilyn Baker
Arr. Christopher Norton

97. Jesus is my Saviour
(medley)

Let God arise: Elizabeth Bacon *(taken from Psalm 68 v.1)*
It's a new day: Unknown

Unknown
Arr. Jeanne Harper

♩ = 92

Boisterously

Refrain: (May be repeated if desired at the beginning and end of this part of medley)

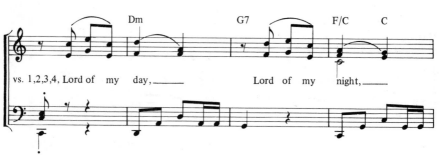

(Accompany with claps and/or wood blocks)

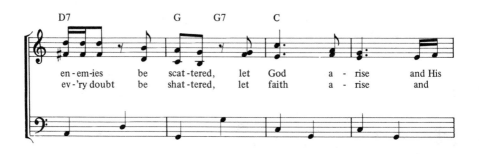

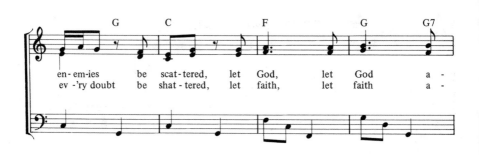

98. Korean song

Korean Folk song
Michael Harper
Arr. Christopher Norton

An old Korean folksong call 'Arirang'-'hill of tears'.
Copyright © 1985 Korean Embassy, 4 Palace Gate, London W8 5NF, by kind permission.
Words copyright © 1986 Michael Harper, 27 Muster Green, Haywards Heath, Sussex RH16 4AL.

99. Peace I give to you

Capo 1 (A)

♩ = 88

Graham Kendrick

Quietly, at a steady pace

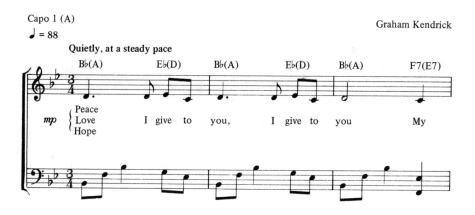

Peace / Love / Hope — I give to you, I give to you My

1. peace. / love. / hope.   2. peace. / love. / hope.   Let it flow to one an-

-oth - er, let it flow, let it flow, let it flow.

Other words may be added: Joy, Grace, Power.

100. Rejoice!

Graham Kendrick
Arr. Christopher Norton

1. Now is the time for us to march upon the land, into our
2. God is at work in us, His purpose to perform, building a
3. Though we are weak, His grace is ev-'ry-thing we need; we're made of

hands He will give the ground we claim.
king-dom of pow-er, not of words,
clay, but this trea-sure is with-in.

He rides in ma-jes-ty to lead us in-to vic-to-ry,
where things im-poss-i-ble by faith shall be made poss-i-ble;
He turns our weak-ness-es in-to our op-por-tu-ni-ties,

the world shall see that Christ is Lord! Re-
let's give the glo-ry to Him now.
so that the glo-ry goes to Him.

101. Ruah

102. Seek My face

Steven Wray

The song should start quietly and build to a climax in verse 4, afterwards decreasing.

This instrumental descant (for either treble recorder or flute) may be added during verses 3 and 4.

103. Signs and wonders
(My God can do anything)

John Pantry
Arr. Christopher Norton

104. Simple gifts
(Shaker song)

American Trad.
Arr. Roland Fudge

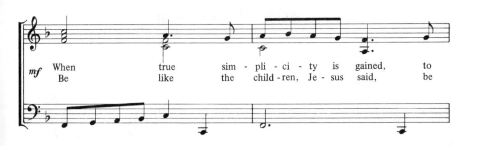

mf When true sim - pli - ci - ty is gained, to
Be like the child - ren, Je - sus said, be

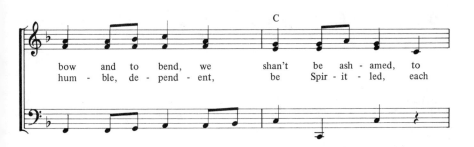

C

bow and to bend, we shan't be ash - amed, to
hum - ble, de - pend - ent, be Spir - it - led, each

F ✻

turn, turn will be our de - light, till by
day, then, will be full of peace and you'll

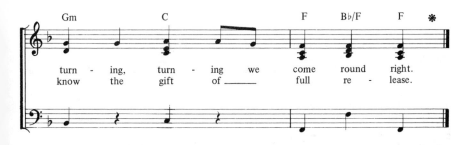

Gm C F Bb/F F ✻

turn - ing, turn - ing we come round right.
know the gift of ____ full re - lease.

Some may like to repeat from 𝄋 and end at ⊕ .
✻ ✻This section may be played between verses.

105. Spirit song

♩ = 92

John Wimber

Worshipfully
Moderately slow

mf 1. Oh, let the Son of God en - fold you with His
sing this song with glad - ness as your

Spir - it and His love. Let Him fill your heart and
hearts are filled with joy. Lift your hands in sweet sur -

sat - is - fy your soul. Oh, let Him
ren - der to His name. Oh, give Him

have the things that hold you and His Spir - it, like a
all your tears and sad - ness, give Him all your years of

106. Step by step

Peter Sandwall
Arne Höglund

107. Sweet perfume

John Wimber

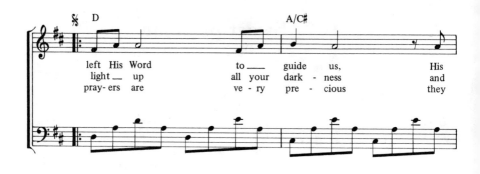

left His Word to ___ guide us, His
light ___ up all your dark - ness and
pray- ers are ve - ry pre - cious they

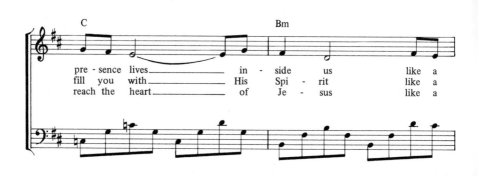

pre - sence lives ___ in - side us like a
fill you with ___ His Spi - rit like a
reach the heart ___ of Je - sus like a

sweet, sweet ___ per -

fume. ___ Don't ev - er

108. Tell My people

♩ = 96

Anon
Verses 1,2 and descant Jan Harrington
Vs. 3-5 Jeanne Harper

With warmth
Refrain

Verse melody

1. Tell My people I came and died
   to give them liberty
   and to abide in Me
   is to be really free.

2. Tell My people where'er they go
   My comfort they can know,
   My peace and joy and love
   I freely will bestow.

3. Tell My people My blood was shed
   their righteousness to win,
   My Spirit came to earth
   to give them power within.

4. Jesus tells us the Kingdom's near –
   Who will His battles fight?
   Those who have Satan's power
   can't touch the sons of light.

5. It is those who have chosen Him
   obedient to His will
   who'll claim the victory
   God's kingdom to fulfil.

109. Vaster far than any ocean

Russian folk melody
Unknown
Arr. Jeanne Harper

♩ = 76

With a lilt

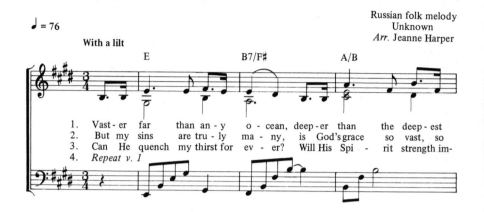

1. Vast-er far than an-y o-cean, deep-er than the deep-est
2. But my sins are tru-ly ma-ny, is God's grace so vast, so
3. Can He quench my thirst for ev-er? Will His Spi - rit strength im-
4. *Repeat v. 1*

sea is the love of Christ my Sa - viour reach-ing
deep? Yes, there's grace o'er sin a - bound-ing, grace to
part? Yes, He gives me liv - ing wat - er, spring - ing

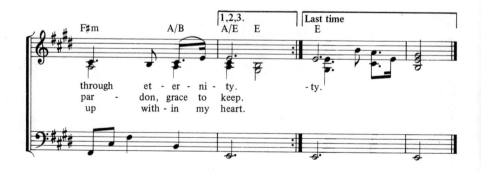

through et - er - ni - ty. - ty.
par - don, grace to keep.
up with - in my heart.

110. You are my hiding place

♩ = 84

Michael Ledner
Arr. Christopher Norton

With quiet strength

mp You are my hid - ing place, You al - ways fill my heart with songs of de - li - ver - ance when - ev - er I am a - fraid, I will trust in You.

I will trust in You; let the weak say, 'I am strong in the strength of the Lord!'

✻ To sing as a round in two parts, Group 2 should begin when Group 1 arrives at this point.

SONGIFTS

5

Songs of Wholeness

111. Breathe on me, breath of God

Capo 1(D)

E. Hatch: 'Trentham'
Arr. Roland Fudge

♩ = 80   With serenity

4. Breathe on me, breath of God,
   so shall I never die,
   but live with You the perfect life
   of Your eternity.

112. Change my heart, oh God

Eddie Espinosa
Arr. James Gabriel Stipech

113. Exodus XV

Frank Gallian
Arr. James Gabriel Stipech

114. Father, lift me up

Honeytree
Arr. Christopher Norton

♩ = 84

1. Like a lit - tle child, Je - sus told me to come and the
(2.) I be lift - ed up from the earth, Je - sus said,
3. If I die to self, Je - sus told me I will live;
4. High up a - bove all pow-ers and all kings,
5. Ho - ly, ho - ly, holy is the Lamb that was slain,

Fath - er lifts me up, up to Hea - ven, up to home.
I will draw ev - ery per - son un - to Me.
cru - ci - fied with Je - sus I want to be.
there is a throne where the faith - ful sing.
through the Ho - ly Spirit, I call up - on His name.

Fath - er, lift me up, all - e - lu - ia,

ho - ly is Your name, Fath - er lift me up, all - e -

lu - ia, ho - ly is Your name. 2. If

115. Father, show Yourself to me

♩ = 88

Paul Anderson
Arr. Christopher Norton

Quietly

1. Fath - er,
2. Je - sus,
3. Spi - rit,

show Your - self to me, _____
live Your life through me, _____
work a - new in me, _____

show Your -
live Your
work a -

self _____ to me.
life _____ through me. *(slower)* _____
new _____ in me.

116. Grace song

Kara Tikka
Transl. Michael Harper
Arr. Jeanne Harper

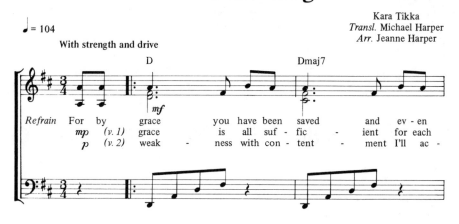

Refrain
For by grace you have been saved and ev - en
(v. 1) grace is all suf - fic - ient for each
(v. 2) weak - ness with con - tent - ment I'll ac -

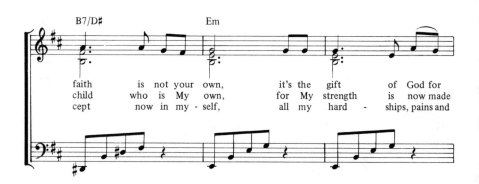

faith is not your own, it's the gift of God for
child who is My own, for My strength is now made
cept now in my - self, all my hard - ships, pains and

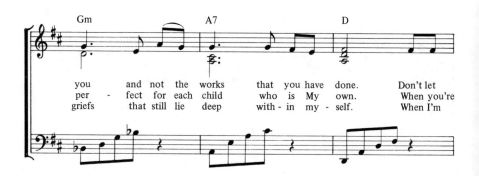

you and not the works that you have done. Don't let
per - fect for each child who is My own. When you're
griefs that still lie deep with - in my - self. When I'm

117. Held

Eithne Dillon
Arr. Christopher Norton

♩ = 80

Worshipfully

1. *(Unison)* Held with-in the hol - low of God's might-y hand,
2. *(Harm.)* Words of ten-der - ness and love, com-fort, calm and still,
3. *(Unacc. Harm.)* Bless - ed Je-sus' ma-jes-ty, com-ing Lord and King

dwell-ing in Your sec - ret place, kept by Your com - mand.
Je - sus, lov - er, Sa - viour, Friend, touch me, make me whole.
from my heart tho' weak and poor, praise to You I'll sing,

(vs. 2, 3:)

cov - ered with Your wings of love, earth's dark sha-dows flee _____
Heav'n and earth may pass a - way, Your words shall re - main, _____
give You hon - our, glor - ious Lamb, wound - ed so, for me, _____

for with You, great joy a - bounds, Sa - viour com - fort me.
Your dear pre - sence, true di - vine, Your sweet pre - cious name.
hon - our, bless - ing, pow'r and might, Yours the vic - to - ry.

118. I receive You

John Lai
Arr. Christopher Norton

119. I'm Yours

Eddie Espinosa
Arr. James Gabriel Stipech

120. Jesus, You are changing me

Capo 2 (D)

Marilyn Baker

♩ = 100

Smooth and lyrical

121. Lord, make me holy

Roland Fudge

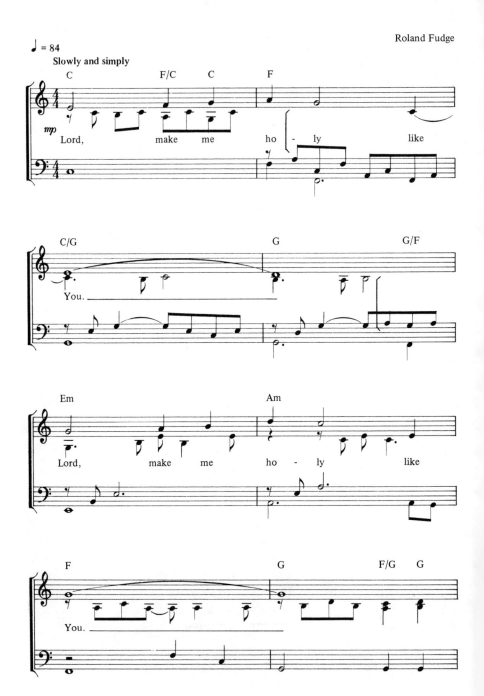

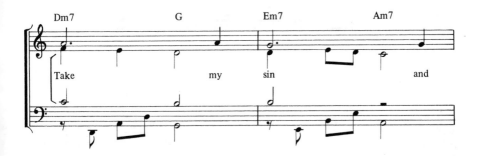

Take my sin and

give to me Your right-eous-ness, Lord, make me

ho - ly like You.

You.

122. Move, Holy Spirit

♩ = 104

Unknown
v. 2 & Arr. Jeanne Harper

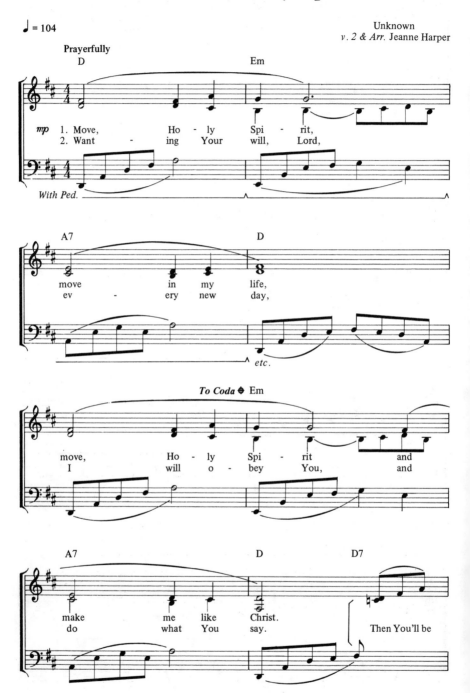

123. Oh Lord, have mercy on me

Carl Tuttle
Arr. Ed Cook

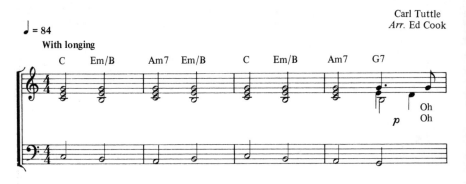

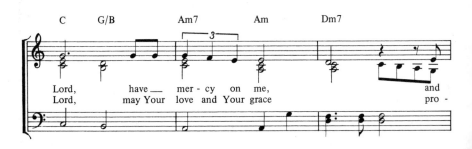

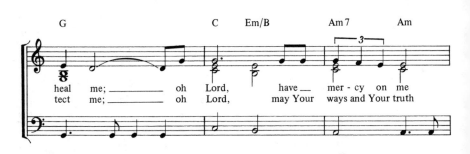

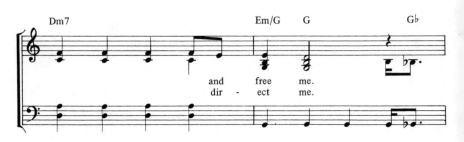

Place my feet u - pon a rock,

put a new song in my heart, in my

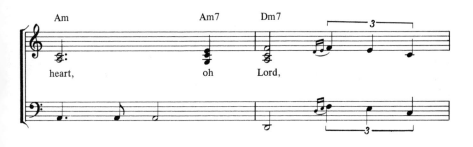

heart, oh Lord,

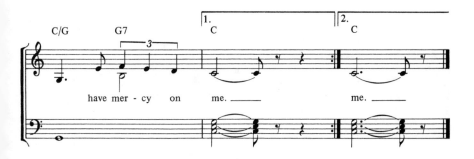

have mer - cy on me. ____ me. ____

124. Oh Lord, You're beautiful

Keith Green

me. O Lord, please light the

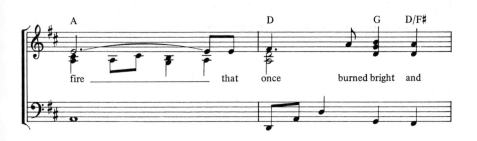

fire _____ that once burned bright and

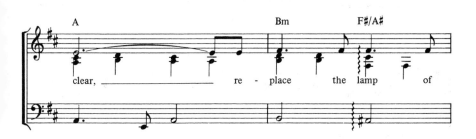

clear, _____ re - place the lamp of

my first love that burns with ho - ly fear.

125. Open my eyes

Michael Hudson
Arr. Jeanne Harper

O - pen my eyes that I may
O - pen my heart that I may

see wonderful things, Lord, in Your
be changed by the word You speak to

Word, O - pen my eyes, o - pen my
me,

heart, o - pen my life to Your Word.

126. Still before Him

This song may be followed by 'Lord, we praise You' (no. 48) in C Major.

127. Tender mercy

Peggy Wagner
Arr. Ed Cook

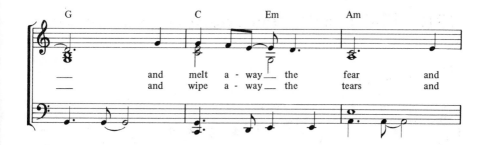

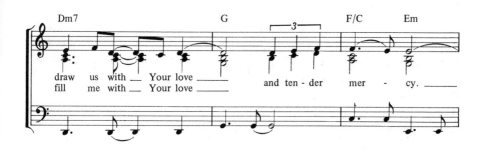

128. The Lord is my strength and my song

Capo 3 (G)

♩ = 66

Roland Fudge

129. The price is paid

Graham Kendrick

$\quad$ = 76

Triumphantly and with breadth

1. The price is paid, come let us en - ter in to all that
   paid, see Sa - tan flee a - way, for Je - sus
   paid, and by that scour-ging cruel, He took our

Je - sus died to make our own. For ev - 'ry sin more than e-nough He
cru - ci - fied des-troys his power. No more to pay, let ac - cus - a - tion
sick - ness-es as if His own. And by His wounds His bo - dy bro - ken

gave, and bought our free - dom from each guil - ty stain.
cease, in Christ there is no con - dem - na - tion now. *The price is*
there, His heal - ing touch may now by faith be known.

paid, all - e - lu - ia, a - maz - ing grace, so strong and

Copyright © 1983 Thankyou Music, P.O. Box 75, Eastbourne BN23 6NW.

4. The price is paid,
   'Worthy the Lamb' we cry,
   Eternity shall never
   Cease His praise.
   The Church of Christ
   Shall rule upon the earth,
   In Jesus' name we have
   Authority.

130. Turn your eyes upon Jesus

Helen Lemmel
Arr. Christopher Norton

SONGIFTS

6

Songs of Proclamation

131. A mighty fortress

Ein' Feste Burg
Martin Luther (1483-1546)
Adapted Michael Perry

♩ = 72

Majestically

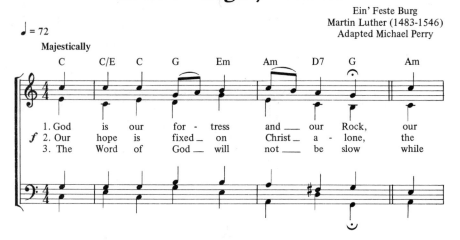

1. God is our for - tress and __ our Rock, our
2. Our hope is fixed __ on Christ __ a - lone, the
3. The Word of God __ will not __ be slow while

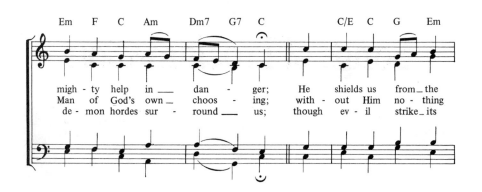

migh - ty help in __ dan - ger; He shields us from __ the
Man of God's own __ choos - ing; with - out Him no - thing
de - mon hordes sur - round __ us; though ev - il strike __ its

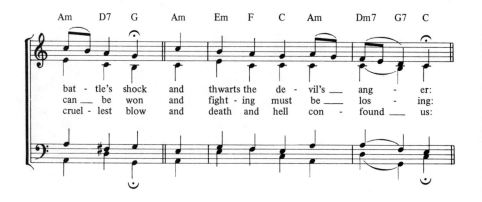

bat - tle's shock and thwarts the de - vil's __ ang - er:
can __ be won and fight - ing must be __ los - ing:
cruel - lest blow and death and hell con - found __ us:

132. Battle hymn

Graham Kendrick
Arr. Christopher Norton

1. There's a

sound on the wind like a vic - to - ry
loud shout of vic - t'ry that leaps from our
crowns for the con - qu'rors and white robes to
King of the a - ges app - roach - es the

song, lis - ten now, let it rest on your soul; _____
hearts, as we wait for our con - quer - ing King, _____
wear, there will be no more sor - row or pain, _____
earth, He will burst through the gates of the sky, _____

_____ it's a song that I learned from a hea - ven - ly
_____ there's a tri - umph re - sound - ing from dark a - ges
_____ and the bat - tle of earth shall be lost in the
_____ and all men shall bow down to His beau - ti - ful

133. Christ the Lord is risen today

Traditional
Arr. Christopher Norton

134. For His name is exalted
(medley)

For Thou, Lord: Pete Sanchez

Capo 3 (D)

♩ = 88

Dale Garratt
Arr. Jeanne Harper
and Christopher Norton

With exaltation

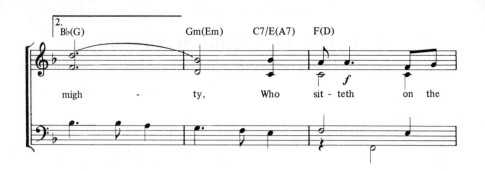

migh - ty, Who sit - teth on the

throne *f* and Who lives for ev - er -

- more. For Thou Lord art

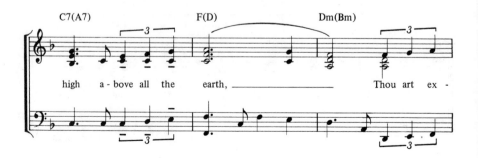

high a - bove all the earth, Thou art ex -

135. Hallelujah song

Frank Hernandez
Arr. Christopher Norton

♪ = 192

Triumphantly

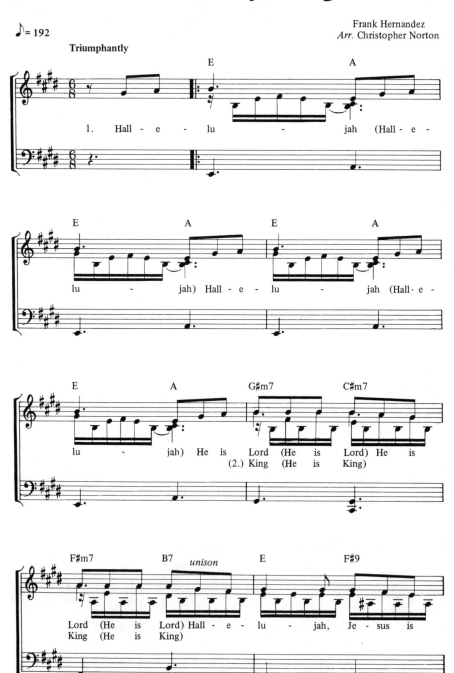

This is a good song for drawing together a group of people into one praising body.

136. Let God arise

137. Oh magnify the Lord
(medley)

Be exalted: Brent Chambers
He is Lord: Martin V. Frey

David Garratt
Arr. R. Fudge

138. Onward, Christian soldiers

S. Baring-Gould
Arr. Christopher Norton

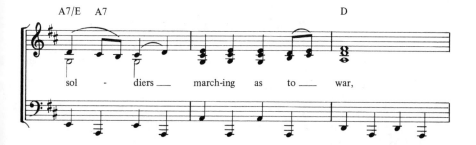

sol - diers ___ march-ing as to ___ war,

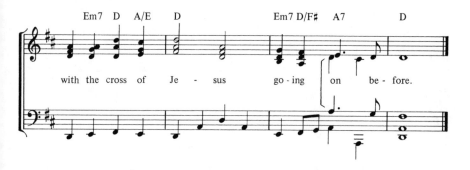

with the cross of Je - sus go - ing on be - fore.

2. At the name of Jesus, Satan's armies flee:
   on then, Christian soldiers, on to victory!
   Hell's foundations tremble at the shout of praise —
   sing the song of triumph! loud your voices raise!

   Onward, Christian soldiers. . .

3. Like a mighty army moves the church of God:
   we are humbly treading where the saints have trod;
   Christ is not divided — all one Body we,
   one in hope and calling, one in charity.

   Onward, Christian soldiers. . .

4. Crowns and thrones may perish, kingdoms rise and wane,
   but the church of Jesus ever shall remain;
   death and hell and Satan never shall prevail —
   We have Christ's own promise, and that cannot fail.

   Onward, Christian soldiers. . .

5. Onward then, you people! march in faith, be strong!
   blend with ours your voices in the triumph song:
   Glory, praise and honour be to Christ the King!
   this through countless ages, men and angels sing.

   Onward, Christian soldiers. . .

139. Our God reigns

140. Possess the land

Capo 2 (C)

♩ = 132

Linda Caroe
Arr. Jeanne Harper

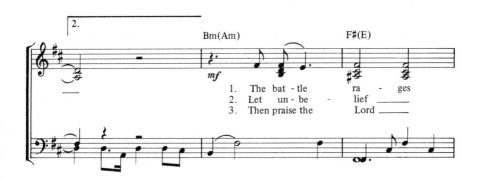

2.

Bm(Am)   F#(E)

mf

1. The bat - tle   ra - ges
2. Let un - be - lief _____
3. Then praise the   Lord _____

Bm(Am)   F#(E)   E(D)

on ev - 'ry hand,   we won't fear,__
and all doubt flee,   we will know__
and bless His name   for His pow -

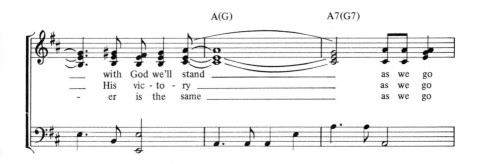

A(G)   A7(G7)

___ with God we'll stand _____ as we go
___ His vic - to - ry _____ as we go
 - er is the same _____ as we go

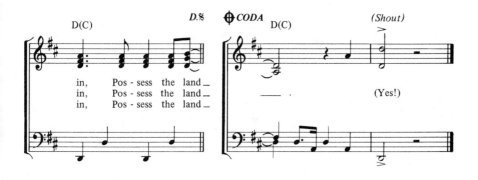

D(C)   *D.%*   CODA D(C)   *(Shout)*

in, Pos - sess the land _
in, Pos - sess the land _
in, Pos - sess the land _   *(Yes!)*

141. Praise is the power of heaven
(medley)

Let there be glory: James & Elizabeth Greenelsch

T. King
Arr. Jeanne Harper

♩ = 104

Strongly

Praise is the pow - er of hea - ven, _____ praise is the pow - er of hea - ven. _____ Praise is the pow - er that o - pens the door _____ to the King, _____ the King _____ of kings. _____

142. Sing to the Lord!

Roland Fudge

143. Through our God

Capo 3 (Am)

Dale Garratt
Arr. Peter Sandwall

♩ = 90

With drive

mf

Very gradually faster

Cm/G(Am)

Thro' our God   we shall do

G7(E7)   Cm/G(Am)

val - iant-ly,   it is He   Who will tread down our e - ne-mies, we'll

144. How majestic is Your name

♩ = 168

Michael W. Smith

O Lord, our Lord,— how ma -

jes - tic is Your name— in all ____ the ____ earth: O

Omit bars between asterisks if desired.

145. We declare Your majesty
(medley)

Ascribe greatness: Unknown

♩ = 112

Majestically

Malcolm du Plessis

mf   We de - clare Your maj - es - ty,_____

_____ we pro - claim that Your name___ is ex -

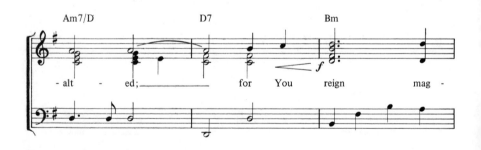

- alt - ed;_____ for You reign mag -

- ni - fi - cent - ly, rule vic - tor - i - ous - ly,

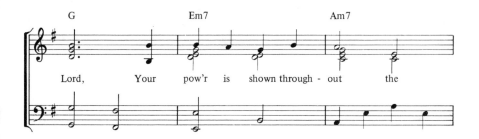

Lord, Your pow'r is shown through - out the

earth. And we ex - claim _____ our God ___ is

might - y, _____ lift up Your name, _____

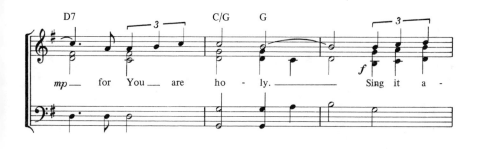

mp — for You ___ are ho - ly. _____ Sing it a -

gain,_____ all hon - our and glo - ry,_____

mf in a - dor - a - tion we bow be - fore Your

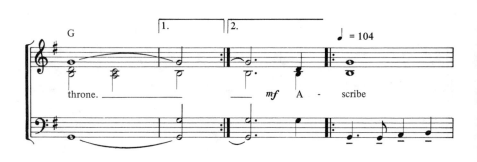

throne._____ _____ *mf* A - scribe

great - ness to our God, the Rock,_____ His work is

per - fect and all His ways are just,_____ as -

_____ a God of faith-ful - ness__ and with - out in -

- just - ice,__ good and up - right is He,_____

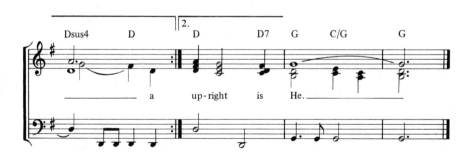

_____ a up - right is He._____

146. We worship You, oh God, in this temple

♩ = 92 (increasing to 138 at *)

Larry Dempsey
Arr. Alan Browning

With quiet strength

147. Yahweh is King

Lenny Smith Jr.
Arr. Christopher Norton

148. You are the King who reigns

David Boyd
Arr. James Gabriel Stipech

♩ = 120

With confidence and strength

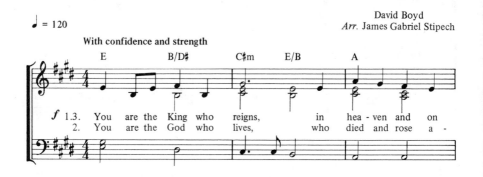

f 1.3. You are the King who reigns, in hea - ven and on
2. You are the God who lives, who died and rose a -

earth. You are the King who reigns, the
gain. You are the God who reigns, who

au - thor of new birth.___
cov - ers all our sins.___

Lord, we sing Your praise, we ex-alt Your

name.   Your_ glo - ry fills this   place,   Your_

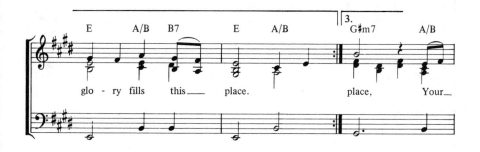

glo - ry fills this_ place.   place,   Your_

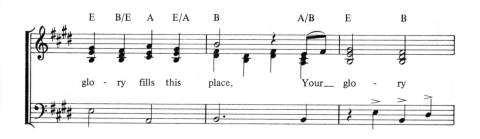

glo - ry fills this   place,   Your_ glo - ry

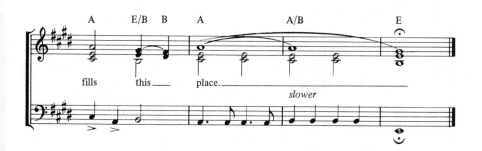

fills   this_ place._

slower

149. The victory way

Jeanne Harper

♩ = 116

Spirited

1. God has giv-en us all that we need,— weapons in-deed,— if we— but heed — His word that says "Let Me on-ly lead— you, give you— the seed,— of trust in your heart."

2. Vic-t'ry is for the ones who are car-ing— for oth-er folk, shar-ing the things that they have,— just giv-ing them-selves a-way— to oth-ers,— to them— they're bro-thers in God's fa-mi-ly. —

3. Je-sus, we'll think a-bout— You al-ways,then You— will cause us to be— like You;— for You were born, Lord, to be the Ex-amp-le— of God's life e-ter-nal, to Him You were true.—

4. Hal-le-lu-jah to God be the glo-ry—for His is the sto-ry whose end-ing is good;— oh hal-le-lu-jah, to God be the glo-ry—for He gives our sto-ry an end-ing that's good.—

to You they'll bring. —

5. Vict'ry to Jesus Christ the King,
He's reigning in heaven,
He owns everything,
come, Lord, now rule over all the nations,
bring them Your salvation,
praise to You they'll bring.

SONGIFTS

7

Songs for Children

150. I want to tell the truth

J. Clowe & J. Cothran
Vv. 2, 5 and arr. Jeanne Harper

♩ = 72

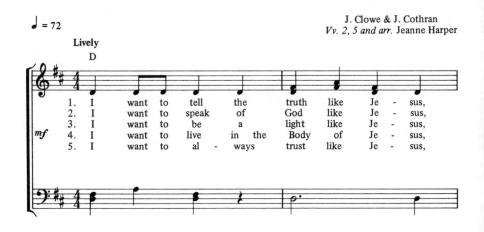

Lively

D

mf

1. I want to tell the truth like Je - sus,
2. I want to speak of God like Je - sus,
3. I want to be a light like Je - sus,
4. I want to live in the Body of Je - sus,
5. I want to al - ways trust like Je - sus,

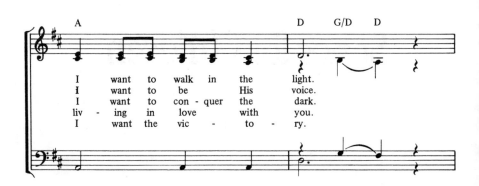

A   D   G/D   D

I want to walk in the light.
I want to be His voice.
I want to con - quer the dark.
liv - ing in love with you.
I want the vic - to - ry.

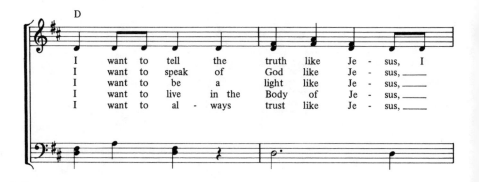

D

I want to tell the truth like Je - sus, I
I want to speak of God like Je - sus, _____
I want to be a light like Je - sus, _____
I want to live in the Body of Je - sus, _____
I want to al - ways trust like Je - sus, _____

151. Jump up and down

Ruth Fazal
Arr. Jeanne Harper

(indicating one another)

love You, ___ tell Him you love Him now. ___

Accompany with tambourines.

152. King of kings and Lord of lords
(A 2-part round)

Unknown

♩ = 108

With energy

King of kings and Lord of ___ lords, ___ glo - ry, hall - e - lu - jah! Je - sus,

Prince of peace, glo - ry, hall - e - lu - jah!

This song may be sung as written and/or the two parts simultaneously as a canon.
To be accompanied with maracas or tambourine.

This song may also be danced in the following manner:

Holding hands in a circle, each person takes a step to the right drawing the feet together to complete the first bar. Repeat for the second bar. Clap, raising the hands slightly on the word 'glory' and stamp feet twice to complete third bar. Repeat for the fourth bar. Repeat these steps for the second phrase, only this time move to the left, and do not clap or stamp.

153. Living the Jesus way

♩ = 112

Walking pace, cheerfully

Linda Caroe
Arr. Jeanne Harper

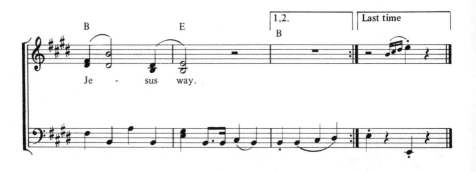

2. Seeing, (seeing), helping, (helping),
Loving, (loving), trusting, (trusting),
Living the Jesus way.

3. Praying, (praying), obeying, (obeying),
Loving, (loving), forgiving, (forgiving),
Living the Jesus way.

Actions are suggested indicating the stages of the Christian life described in the verses.

Caring	Sharing	Loving	Giving

Living the Jesus way

Seeing	Helping	Loving	Trusting

Living the Jesus way

Praying	Obeying	Loving	Forgiving

Living the Jesus way

154. Praise the Lord

♩ = 142

Christopher Norton/
Murray Watts

155. Sing heaven

On repeat, men sing 'Sing heaven' while ladies sing 'Alleluia',
then ladies sing 'Sing heaven' while men sing 'Alleluia'.

156. Sing to Him
(a round)

♩ = 120

Sylvia Lawton

Sing to Him, sing prais - es to Him,

tell of _____ all His won - der - ful works.

Accompany with bells.

157. The stars danced

Barbara Gillard
Arr. V. Fleetwood

♩ = 120

1. The stars danced, the an - gels sang the
2. Ma - ry, His mo - ther smiled to
3. Wise men who saw His star,
4. We too will give to Him,

night God came to earth._____ The whole vault of
see her babe new - born._____ Shep - herds came
knew their Lord was here, _____ came with their
gifts of love and praise._____ Dance for Him,

158. When the Spirit of the Lord

Stand in a circle:—

Left foot to the left   Right is drawn behind   Repeat
it, in order to 'bob.'

Repeat this, moving to the right.

Right foot crossing the left, skip to the left with hands joined:—

At the end of the repeat of this second half move towards the centre still skipping, and end with two claps high in the air, then shout 'Oi' (— Increase the speed of each verse until this climax.)

159. There's new life in Jesus

Max Dyer
Arr. Jeanne Harper

1. There's new life in Je - sus, lift up your heart!
2. There is heal - ing in His love, lift up your heart!
3. There is free - dom in His praise, lift up your heart!

Lift up your heart, lift up your heart.

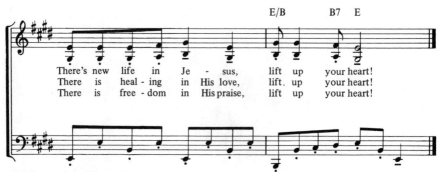

There's new life in Je - sus, lift up your heart!
There is heal - ing in His love, lift up your heart!
There is free - dom in His praise, lift up your heart!

This is a good song for each person to minister encouragement to his neighbours in a meeting. Add other verses as appropriate.

SONGIFTS

8

Songs for Special Occasions

160. Angels praise Him

Capo 5 (A)

♩ = 80

Norman Warren
Michael Perry

With a swing

1. An - gels praise Him, hea - vens praise Him,
3. Winds praise Him, fire praise Him,
5. Earth praise Him, moun - tains praise Him,

wa - ters praise Him,
heat praise Him, } hall - e - lu - jah!
hills praise Him,

pow - ers of the Lord all praise Him
win - ter praise Him, sum - mer praise Him
green things praise Him, wells praise Him

for ev - er - more.
for ev - er - more.
for ev - er - more.

2. Sun praise Him,
4. Nights praise Him,
6. Seas praise Him,

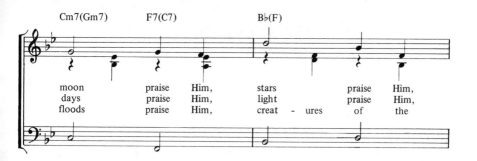

moon praise Him, stars praise Him,
days praise Him, light praise Him,
floods praise Him, creat - ures of the

hal - le - lu - jah! showers praise Him,
dark - ness praise Him, light - nings praise Him,
wa - ters praise Him, birds, beasts and

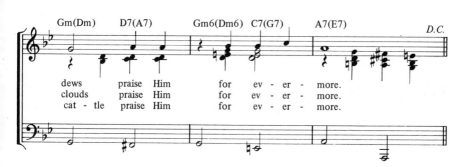

dews praise Him for ev - er - more.
clouds praise Him for ev - er - more.
cat - tle praise Him for ev - er - more.

7. Nations praise Him,
Churches praise Him,
Saints praise Him,
Hallelujah!
All His people
Join to praise Him
For evermore.

161. Bless the Lord

♩ = 92

Berj Topalian

With movement

Bless the Lord, oh my soul, bless His ho - ly name!
(bless the Lord)

Fine

Ev - er - last - ing is His love from age to age the same.
For - He

get not all His be - ne - fits, He par - dons all your sin, He
crowns you with His stead-fast love, He fills you with good things, Your

heals your in - firm - i - ties, re - deems you from death's sting.
vig - our dai - ly He re - news, you rise on ea - gles' wings.

162. Fill us

Unknown
Arr. Jeanne Harper

Basic speed ♩ = 88

163. God of gods, we sound His praises

♩ = 112

Christian Strover

Strongly

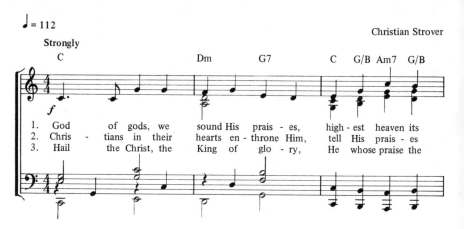

1. God of gods, we sound His prais - es, high - est heaven its
2. Chris - tians in their hearts en - throne Him, tell His prais - es
3. Hail the Christ, the King of glo - ry, He whose praise the

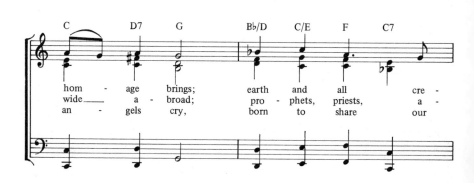

hom - age brings; earth and all cre -
wide a - broad; pro - phets, priests, a -
an - gels cry, born to share our

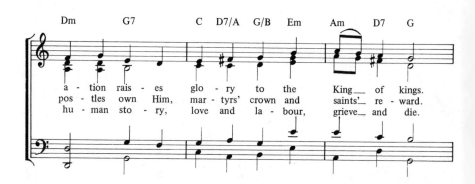

a - tion rais - es glo - ry to the King of kings.
pos - tles own Him, mar - tyrs' crown and saints' re - ward.
hu - man sto - ry, love and la - bour, grieve and die.

Ho - ly, ho - ly, ho - ly, name Him, Lord of all His hosts pro - claim Him, to the ev - er - last - ing Fa - ther ev - ery tongue in tri - umph sings.

Three in one His glo - ry shar - ing, earth and heav'n His praise de - clar - ing, praise the high ma - jes - tic Fa - ther, praise the ev - er - last - ing Lord.

By His cross His work com - plet - ed, sin - ners ran - somed, death de - feat - ed, in the glo - ry of the Fa - ther Christ as - cend - ed, reigns on high.

4. Lord, we look for Your returning,
    Teach us so to walk Your ways,
    Hearts and minds Your will discerning,
    Lives alight with joy and praise.
    In Your love and care enfold us,
    By Your constancy uphold us,
    May Your mercy, Lord and Father,
    Keep us now and all our days.

164. Hymn to the Spirit

♩ = 96

Soaring

Stainer

Words and descant: John Richards

1. Spirit, working in creation,
   Bringing order out of strife,
   Come around God's gathered people,
   Giving harmony and life.

2. Spirit, speaking through the prophets
   So the voice of God was heard,
   Come, inspire, alert|Your people
   To today's prophetic word.

3. Spirit, overshad'wing Mary
   As the Christ-child in her grew,
   Come, so that the Christ within us
   May today be born anew.

4. Spirit, coming from the Father
   As a dove upon our Lord,
   Come upon Your favoured people
   And Your blessings be outpoured.

5. Spirit, driving to the desert
   Even God's Anointed One,
   Come to us in trial and testing
   That God's will in us be done.

6. Spirit, bringing freedom, blessing,
   Help to poor and health to lame,
   Come, anoint us, that such wonders
   May be done in Jesus' name.

Additional verse for
Holy Communion service

7. Spirit, taking, breaking, making
   Bread and wine our heavenly food,
   Come, and take us, break us, make us,
   Live Christ's life in us renewed.

8. Spirit, breathed on the disciples
   Giving peace where there was fear,
   Come amongst us, touch us, send us,
   Making Jesus' presence near.

Additional verse for
Confirmation service

9. Spirit, coming to Christ's servants
   To confirm, equip, empower,
   Come upon us, and the churches
   For our witness at this hour.

10. Spirit, wind and flame, empow'ring
    Fearless witness to the lost,
    Come, unite, renew Your wonders
    As of a new Pentecost!

11. Praise and glory, Holy Spirit,
    For Your love on us outpoured,
    Giving honour to the Father,
    And proclaiming Jesus — LORD.

Christopher Norton
John Richards

♩ = 104

Peacefully

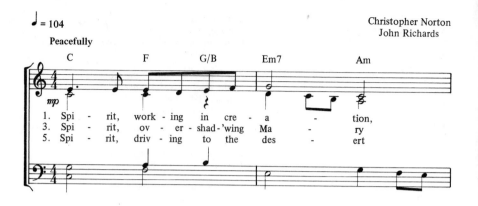

```
            C           F      G/B      Em7              Am
mp
1. Spi -   rit,   work - ing   in   cre - a       -    tion,
3. Spi -   rit,   ov - er - shad - 'wing  Ma   -        ry
5. Spi -   rit,   driv - ing   to   the   des   -      ert
```

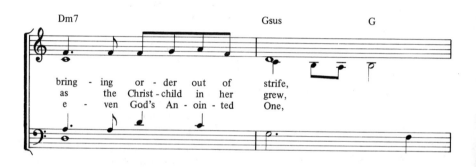

```
   Dm7                              Gsus            G
bring - ing   or - der   out   of   strife,
  as     the  Christ - child  in  her  grew,
  e  -   ven  God's  An - oin - ted   One,
```

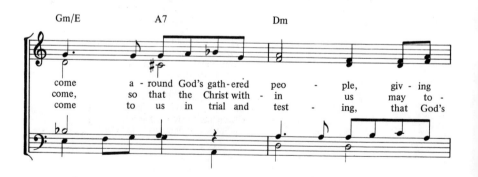

```
   Gm/E          A7              Dm
come       a - round  God's gath - ered   peo   -   ple,   giv - ing
come,      so   that  the  Christ with - in   us   may   to -
come       to   us    in   trial  and   test   -   ing,   that  God's
```

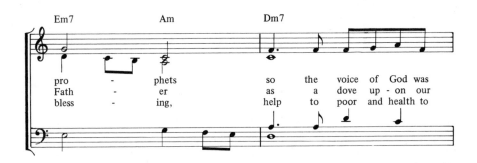

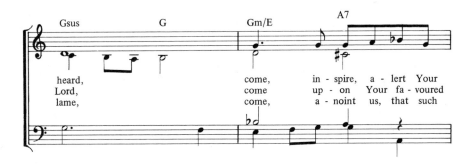

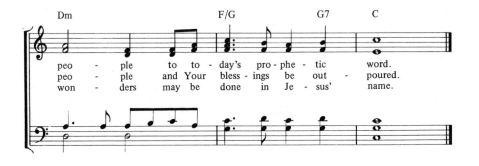

165. Living Lord

♩ = 104

Christopher Norton
Jill Jenkins

Steadily

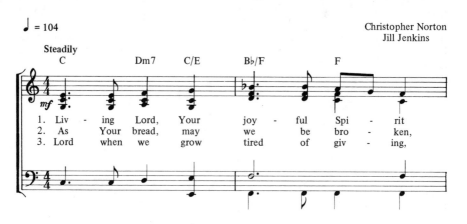

1. Liv - ing Lord, Your joy - ful Spi - rit
2. As Your bread, may we be bro - ken,
3. Lord when we grow tired of giv - ing,

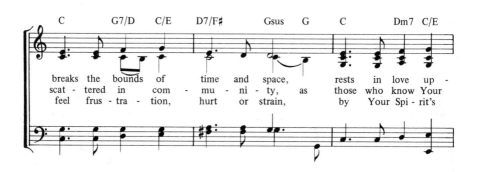

breaks the bounds of time and space, rests in love up -
scat - tered in com - mu - ni - ty, as those who know Your
feel frus - tra - tion, hurt or strain, by Your Spi - rit's

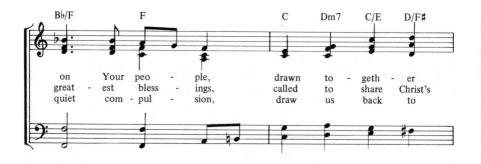

on Your peo - ple, drawn to - geth - er
great - est bless - ings, called to share Christ's
quiet com - pul - sion, draw us back to

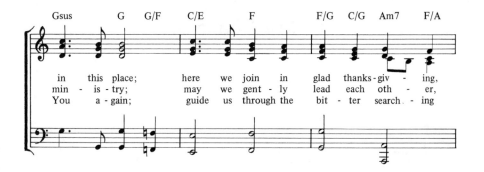

| Gsus | G | G/F | C/E | F | | F/G | C/G | Am7 | F/A |

in this place; here we join in glad thanks-giv - ing,
min - is - try; may we gent - ly lead each oth - er,
You a - gain; guide us through the bit - ter search - ing

| C/B♭ | F/A | C/G | D7/F♯ | | Gsus | G | C | B♭/D | C7/E |

here re - joice to pray and praise, Lord of all our
share our hun - ger and our thirst, learn that on - ly
when our con - fi - dence is lost, life and hope from

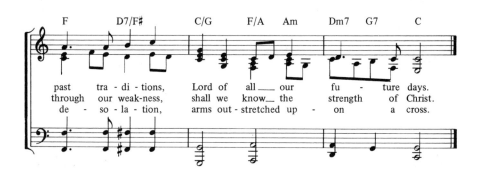

| F | D7/F♯ | | C/G | F/A | Am | Dm7 | G7 | C |

past tra - di - tions, Lord of all ___ our fu - ture days.
through our weak-ness, shall we know___ the strength of Christ.
de - so - la - tion, arms out - stretched up - on a cross.

4. Living Lord, Your power surrounds us,
   As we face the way Christ trod,
   Challenge us to fresh commitment
   As the servant-sons of God,
   Called to share a new creation,
   Called to preach a living Word,
   Promised all the joys of heaven,
   Through the grace of Christ our Lord.

166. Lord have mercy

Gerard Markland
Arr. Roland Fudge

167. Mercy and truth

♩ = 88

Marty Nystrum
Arr. Peter Sandwall

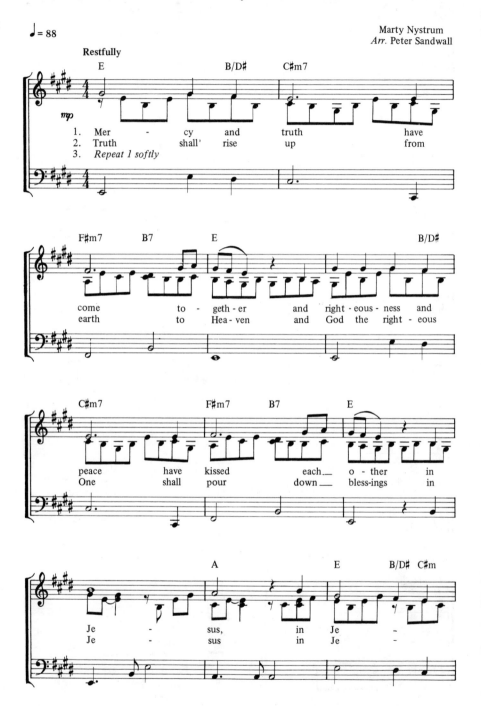

Restfully

1. Mer - cy and truth have
2. Truth shall' rise up from
3. *Repeat 1 softly*

come to - geth - er and right - eous - ness and
earth to Hea - ven and God the right - eous

peace have kissed each__ o - ther in
One shall pour down__ bless-ings in

Je - sus, in Je -
Je - sus in Je -

sus, ____ in Je - sus the Lamb that was

sus, ____ in Je - sus the Lamb that was

Last time:

slain.

slain.

168. O adoramus te Domine

♩ = 76

Taizé Community (France)

Slow

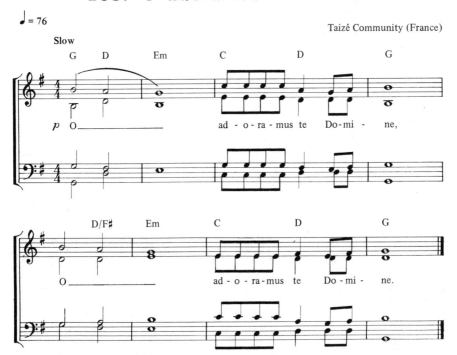

p O ____ ad - o - ra - mus te Do - mi - ne,

O ____ ad - o - ra - mus te Do - mi - ne.

Slightly amended with permission.

For use during Communion, starting very softly and increasing in intensity until the last person has received, when it may be sung as a final act of praise.

169. Our Father

♩ = 84

At a steady pace

John Marsh
Arr. Christopher Norton

Our Fath - er in hea - ven, hal - lowed be Your_ name, Your king - dom_ come, Your will be_ done, on earth as in_ heaven. Give us to-day our_ dai-ly bread, for - give us our_ sins, as we for - give those who

170. Preserve us, O Lord

♩ = 80

David McGregor
Arr. Christopher Norton

Gently

Pre - serve us, O Lord, while wak - ing and guard us while sleep - ing, that a - wake we may watch with Christ and a - sleep we may rest in peace.

slow down

171. This is the day

♩ = 142

Unknown
Arr. Jeanne Harper

With spirit

mf

This is the day that the Lord has made, we will re - joice and be

172. Worthy

♩ = 76

With a gentle lilt

Rich Cook

1. Wor - thy, wor - thy, wor - thy is the Lamb! Worthy is the Lamb!
2. Glo - ry, glo - ry, glo - ry to His name! Glory to His name!
3. Ho - ly, ho - ly, ho - ly is the Lord! Holy is the Lord!
4. Praise Him, praise Him, praise Him ev - er - more! Praise Him ev - er - more!
5. Je - sus, Je - sus, Je - sus is my Lord! Jesus is my Lord!
6. Thank Him, thank Him, thank Him ev - er - more! Thank Him ev - er - more!

173. Worthy, worthy, worthy

♩ = 92

Rick Ridings

Serenely

Wor - thy, wor -

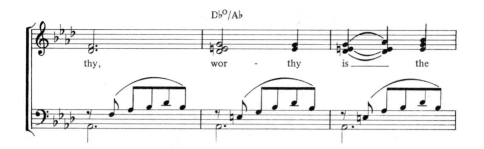
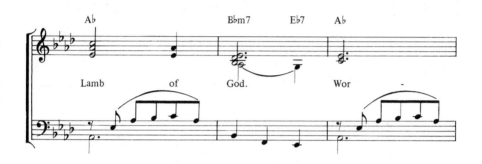
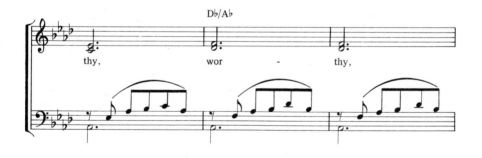
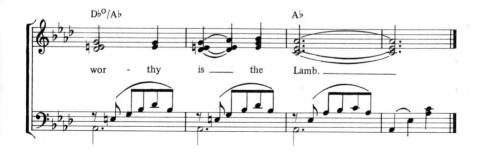

174. Worthy is the Lamb

♩ = 76

Unknown
Arr. Roland Fudge

optional descant last verse:–

Glo-ry to the Lamb; glo-ry to the Lamb; glo-ry to the Lamb. —

optional vocal harmonies,
verse 2 & 4:

TOPICAL INDEX

SONGS FROM COUNTRIES OTHER THAN THE UK AND USA

ii

WORSHIP LEADERS' GUIDE

iii

OPTIONAL ADDITIONAL INSTRUMENTS

INDEX OF TITLES AND FIRST LINES

First lines are included in italics if they differ from the titles.